TRAIL-BLAZERS OF SCIENCE

TRAIL-BLAZERS OF SCIENCE

Life Stories of Some Half-Forgotten
Pioneers of Modern Research

By
MARTIN GUMPERT

Translated From the German by
EDWIN L. SHUMAN

Essay Index Reprint Series

 BOOKS FOR LIBRARIES PRESS
FREEPORT, NEW YORK

First Published 1936
Reprinted 1968

LIBRARY OF CONGRESS CATALOG CARD NUMBER:

68-29212

PRINTED IN THE UNITED STATES OF AMERICA

INTRODUCTION

THIS book presents a group of human documents from the domain of science with a view to demonstrating the ineradicable opposition to genius. Nothing in it is invented: no word, no fact, no figure. It attempts to keep the statement of facts in the world of research free from coloring of every kind, for there has been enough misinterpretation of great events and great men in the sphere of intellectual creation.

The psychologizing of our century is an inveterate vice—a pest. The yoking up of works of art and thought and their backgrounds in the banal terminology of the popular psychological system means at bottom nothing but a heaping up of base calumnies against the intellectually great.

Emotional suffering takes on through this psychological juggling something degradingly common and at the same time unbearably pathetic, so that every trait of inferiority in training and deportment, by an "understanding," is glorified and excused. The mere

v

idea that every disturbance of the emotional life can be explained psychologically is the source of a hypochondria which frivolously and weakly destroys the divine and creative power of man to suffer as stoically as an animal.

My collection is patchwork, a very fragmentary attempt to present the outlines of modern scientific research. For this purpose I have given preference to the scientist who had to fight and suffer as the discoverer of a new or dangerous truth.

The biographical character of the individual chapters makes it necessary to omit some famous names or to give them only fleeting mention. The chronological arrangement of these life stories, from the chaotic Cardan of the Renaissance to the technical-intellectual achievement of our contemporary Cushing, makes it possible to give an inkling of the course of the great battle which mankind has waged within the short period of recorded history in a single domain —that of physical science. It is a portrayal of the unconquerableness of the soul and the inevitability of progress in accordance with a superhuman plan, in spite of the agony and physical annihilation of the poor individual.

M. G.

CONTENTS

vii

Science is eternal in its out-gushing stream, bounded by neither time nor space, immeasurable in its activity, endless in its scope, its final goal ever unreached.

KARL ERNST VON BAER

(*Glances at the Evolution of Science,* St. Petersburg, 1864)

JEROME CARDAN

A Scientist Between the Ages

I

JEROME CARDAN

A Scientist Between the Ages

GOETHE classes Cardan among those men concerning whom we can never come to a unanimous verdict. "Born with great qualities," he says, "Cardan was yet unable to rise to a symmetrical stature; there was always something wild and confused in his studies, his character, and his whole being. Yet, while one finds in him so much that is blameworthy, one must give him great credit for the fact that he was in earnest—often in bitter earnest—concerning the world around him as well as concerning himself, and that on this account his handling of circumstances as well as of life was vehement and passionate to the end.

"He knew his own nature up to a certain point, but until his last years he could not become its master. In thinking of him, his surroundings, and his struggles, we are very often reminded of Cellini, the more so as they both lived at the same time." *

* Goethe, *Materials for a History of the Theory of Colors.*

3

"I count it among the greatest and strangest of natural events,' says Cardan himself in his autobiography, "that I came into the world in the century when the whole circuit of the globe was discovered, whereas to my forefathers only about one third of it was known. . . . Until all these domains are rightly divided up there will surely be a great deal of strife.

"Knowledge and imagination are increasing, but the good arts are forced back and held in low esteem, and the certain is bartered for the uncertain. Is there anything more wonderful than the discovery of gunpowder, this thunderbolt in man's hand, more destructive than that of heaven itself? Thee will I not forget, great magnet, who leadest us over the wide seas, through night and fearful storms, safely into strange and unknown lands. And here let us name also the invention of the printing press. Human hands have done all this, the human mind has made discoveries that emulate the miracles of heaven. What do we still lack to storm heaven itself? Insanity of man, if we do not perceive what is vain and worthless, what weighty and essential!"

Great discoveries are like catastrophes of nature, a mixture of destruction and beneficence. After the misery of the overthrow comes the glory of building up. Throwing the affairs of men out of joint separates the foolish from the wise, the helpless from the strong. The medieval fetters of a thousand years are burst asunder. The "eternal" reign of Greek philosophy, the world of Plato and Aristotle, the medicine of "Church Father" Galen, and the healing art of the Arab Avicenna, all now stiff with dogma, are overthrown by the shock of new actualities.

Where hitherto Petrarch's song of hate against the incompetency of physicians resounded in the ear (*Invectivae contra Medicum quendam*, 1352), or derision of the primitive magic of urine examination, of alchemy and astrology, new problems now appear: new illnesses, new herbs. Syphilis lands in the ports of Europe and scourges lust. The methods of Galen fail. Bodies are dissected, and this bold act reveals a new, terrifying world. Paracelsus begins his revolutionary crusade against the healing art of the time.

The turmoil of the world, a growing power of the masses, a flood of widening energy, these bring war to Europe. The mercenaries of France and the Hapsburgs storm the gates of Italy with an elementary power to which the culture, moderation and individualism of the Renaissance have to succumb. In the North, Luther nails his theses to the church door. The peasants slash at their oppressors. Reformation and Counter-Reformation strew blood and burnings upon the purity of the faith.

In this tumult lived the physician Jerome Cardan—Girolamo Cardano in Italian. His autobiography is one of the most characteristic and memorable documents of the beginning of modern science, far more substantial than all the other significant units among his works. The peculiarity of this masterpiece is its author's fanatically objective way of treating himself—a sort of portrayal that omits nothing, hesitates at nothing —a portrayal that must be called "natural-scientific" in the modern sense of the term. Through Cardan man again became an object of research, an animal to be subjected to experiment and critical investigation. "He speaks of himself, his sensual passions, his falsities, his need of revenge, as a student of nature speaks of the inborn traits of a beast of prey, with the same calm theoretical detachment as that with which Spinoza later depicted the passions." (Dilthey.)

The minute details for which we are indebted to this autobiography melt into each other to form a relentless picture of a chaotic character that dwelt between the ages. Thus he becomes a prototype of the scholarship of that epoch-making crisis out of which modern physical science was to be born. Hunger and poverty, treachery and grief, persecution and prison have no effect on him; they change not for a moment the course of his thought or the goal of his searching. With him begins the great, never-ending conquest-march of the human mind, whose trail this book is to follow.

But while others are ruled by a fixed idea, Cardan is still dominated by impulse—an impulse that laboriously yet unerringly acquires direction. In the world of natural science the work of Cardan is like the creation on the first day. The inmost core of his being shudders under the compulsion with which his depressed and often desolate spirit, ready for every manner of error and weakness, is driven again and again to untiring labor upon the picture of nature taking shape under his hand. Though his work must remain patchwork, painted as it is against the still-deep shadows of an outworn age, it strives, with its sure touch, to set forth on that background his descriptive methods, his departure from Galen, the results of his technical discoveries at the beginning of a new era. Cardan's passion for seeing and judging himself and things, for telling and demanding facts, his struggle between animal nothingness and the inspiring torment of a spiritual existence—these provided the primitive form of the substance out of which the searchers of the following century drew their creative power.

Cardan's body: On a long thin neck sits a head with a broad brow, blond short-clipped hair, a divided chin-beard, little, blinking eyes, a loud and raucus voice, a bullet-shaped swelling on his neck, a flapping, worn-out coat.

His left hand is beautiful, with long, slender, shapely fingers, but his right hand is plump and formless, and the life line in it is short. The astrologers say he will not survive his fortieth year. This prediction impresses him deeply, for he believes in signs and omens. The position of the stars at his birth was not propitious. Almost dead, with black coarse hair, he came into the world at Pavia on September 24, 1500, after drugs to cause a miscarriage had been used without success. The mother was highstrung, small, fat, pious. His father, Fazio, a lawyer, wore with credit the purple robe of his profession, lost his teeth early, persistently wore a cap, was stoop-shouldered, studied Euclid with ardor and limited understanding. He asserted repeatedly that he was in communication with an evil spirit. He treated his son as a slave. Jerome had to accompany him everywhere and serve him constantly. When at the age of eight he fell ill of an epidemic raging in Milan, whither the family had moved, he was saved by his father's prayers to St. Jerome, for his father had a pious heart. Between grievous blows and tender affection his youth was spent.

Until the age of nineteen Cardan remained the servant of his father—a sickly, weak servant in the hands of a pedantic but not always ill-natured master.

Then he went to the University of Pavia, began to study law, but soon saw the vast province of natural science spread out before his eyes, the world meaning and life significance of humanism, which revealed medicine, mathematics, technics, and ethics all growing out of the same root into the eternity of heaven.

As a student Cardan went through the classes of the little university, which was then dying of the terrible deprivations of war. Envied because of his freedom from poverty, he was feared by his friends and hated by his teachers on account of the sharpness and clarity of his judgments, the boundlessness of his ambition, and his haughty disdain of fear and fate. For death and famine and a painful sense of insecurity and change were gripping everyone else by the throat.

An angler, a playboy, a lazy do-nothing, he could suddenly change himself into a busy and purposeful man. Death meant to him merely a protective coloring for the soul, a winter sleep for the future. He mastered the power to do nothing with the same ability as the power to work. In no depths and on no heights did he ever let himself get out of hand.

From Pavia young Cardan went to Padua. His father died. Around Milan war raged, and misfortune fell upon the city and upon the arms of its princes, the Visconti and Sforzas. Cardan scattered cash, bought himself friends, fine clothes, costly writing materials, rare books and tender meats. At the age of twenty-four he was elected head master of a school. The young, unlovable, ill-natured, unbalanced man, ambitious, without family, arrogantly wise, found only enviers and enemies. In trying for his degree of doctor of medicine he failed twice; only on the third and last ballot, beyond which no more were allowed, did he finally triumph.

Cardan abandoned city life at twenty-six and lived until his thirty-second year in the little town of Sacco on the slender income of a country doctor and the gifts of certain patrons. It was the "blooming, most beautiful stage of my earthly sojourn," he says. "I played, indulged in music, went walking, ate, buried myself occasionally in my studies, had no hardships or sorrows, was cared for and honored and had friendly intercourse with prominent Venetians."

Cardan's catalog of small joys was prepared in the little town of Sacco while apocalyptic terrors were devastating his Milan home. There the plague was raging, deadly famine tormented the citizens, no one could pay the price of the official grain certificates, and unbearable taxes took all that was left.

Scarcely had the turmoil around Milan begun to abate when Cardan returned thither to practise medicine. But the College of Physicians showed him the door. He made enemies of the influential family of Barbiani, the only ones who could help him. His mother received him coldly, fearing a new burden, and soon he was sitting again in Sacco, a little poorer and a good deal more discouraged.

One night Cardan sees in a dream a magnificent garden, flower-bedecked and richly laden with fruit. He stands before the open gate. A maiden appears. He embraces her, kisses her. But immediately after the first kiss the gardener comes and shuts the gate. Earnestly he implores that it be opened. In vain! So he sees himself, sad and still hanging on the maiden's neck, locked out of paradise.

A few days later a fire breaks out at night in a neighboring house. The house belongs to a man named Aldobelli Bandarini, commander of a Venetian troop of mercenaries. He watches the house burn without stirring a finger, because he "does not like the man." Again after a very few days he sees the daughter of this man, and her face and clothes are those of his dream maiden!

Cardan took the beautiful Lucia Bandarini to wife in 1531 and lived with her for fifteen years. "The unholy dream of the closed gate, however, has become the source of all the sorrows that fell upon me in my later years. I know not whether it was a divine decree or whether it is the expiation for my sins and those of my father. For I myself was hard as steel and have remained master, too, over all the misfortunes that have befallen me."—The door to the small joys had been slammed shut.

The family which he had founded in Sacco under such dubious circumstances became his Nemesis. His eldest son, Giambattista, died under the sword of the executioner. The other, Aldo, "was guilty of crimes and follies that could hardly be surpassed," he writes. "More than once I was compelled to throw him into prison, to shut him out of our home, to disinherit him." His daughter Chiara was childless.

Cardan found the right word for himself: "I have a cold heart and a hot head." It is a magnificently apt definition of the man of science. With a warm heart one can incite or encourage and can practise the deceptive art of suggestion so useful in healing, but only the restless, disturbing mind can search out new ways and achieve a great discovery.

With his young wife Cardan removed from Sacco to Milan. There, instead of bread he found endless lawsuits and contentions. The College of Physicians could not be induced to recognize the poor outsider as a doctor. He fled to the little nest of Gallarate, but after a few months was back again, taking on a patient here and there illegally for a handful of small coins, and, like a conspirator, reading mathematics, geography and architecture before an irregular group of people greedy for knowledge.

In 1538 the course of his life seemed to turn. Through a friend whom he had helped, he was recommended to a Senator and Imperial Counselor, Sfondrati, and the Senator called him to treat his little son, who had long been suffering with convulsions. The famous doctors already in attendance were quite willing to turn over the dying child to this crossroads doctor, Cardan.

The matter ended well. In four days the boy was cured. Moreover, Sfondrati, who was procurator of the College of Physicians, joyfully told of the healing of his son in the Senate, to the governor, to everybody he met, and saw to it that the refractory College accepted him at once as a physician. Cardan actually obtained a salaried position as teacher in the academy and was finally recognized by everybody.

He used this breathing spell from misfortune to burn up everything he had thus far written. We know little of these early works. He regarded them as useless and bad, and destroyed them all, root and branch, except a few medical essays. It was the clearing out of narrow alleys and dark corners that were obstructing the broad avenue which he was to build.

Cardan's work is so vast that the eye can hardly see across it. It is the primitive, bubbly, volcanic earth, still unrecognized by the science of the new time which has covered it up. He could not bear to go without an answer to any question, because he was certain that there was an answer to every question. More than one hundred and thirty of his works, collected into ten massive folio volumes, published by Dr. Charles Spon of Lyons in 1663, have been preserved. Moral science and politics, cultivation of memory, orthography, logic, dialectics, metaphysics, natural history, physics and mathematics, theoretical researches in music, chess and games of hazard, astronomy and astrology, commentaries on medical classics, and numerous studies of theoretical and practical questions of medicine are covered in Cardan's writings. They present one of the most fantastic intellectual landscapes ever created by man. Nowhere did Cardan leave gaps. Beside the discoveries and presentiments of genius, beside his slowly-worked-out and carefully calculated experiments he places on equal terms the boldest and most unattainable imaginary creations of his powerful and untiring brain.

A work that does not aim at workability, that serves no practical purpose, that takes hold of no reader, that can be turned to no public service, this intellectual mountain range has come down to our day almost unnoted and unheeded. And yet the magnificent obsession—the hybrid of this undertaking to reproduce and interpret the picture of nature without a gap and the audacity to fill out the gaps in this system with his own creative mind—earned the lasting monument which his thirst for glory craved. For besides the many successful achievements of his brain he left behind him the rare figure of a scientist who pursued with incredible perseverance his first and original object— the uniting of all nature into a logical whole, from the inanimate elements and the directionless chaos of lust and the senses to the highest forms of social ethics. This will to unity fused creator and idea into one complete and unique whole. As he was, so was his work: something of genius with many shadows and weaknesses, something inconsistent and tense, with many digressions and playtimes, with bitterness, loneliness and sin. Albrecht von Haller, in whose own heart the fever of learning burned, says of Cardan: "Sapientior nemo ubi sapit, dementior nullus ubi errat"—"No one wiser where he is right, no one madder where he is wrong."

One must be thoroughly at home in the edifice of nature to realise Cardan's merits and the significant dates of his creative period. His real achievements often lie scattered and buried under a confused mass of thoughtful and wordy digressions couched in clumsy Latin. In 1539 he came close to the mathematical solution of problems of probability. In 1540 he made the first attempts to ascertain the weight of air; he discovered the electricity of hairs and the laws governing a mirage. In 1545 he described the universal and cross joint, which has come down to us as the cardan joint, though Philo of Byzantium had hit upon its general principle as early as 210 B.C. It made possible the hanging of the compass so that it keeps its balance on a rolling ship, and in the form of the cardan shaft is today a hazy concept in the brain of every auto driver.

In the same year Cardan published a discovery that roused the attention of contemporary scholars and created for him a certain unprofitable fame. In his treatise *Artis Magnae sive de Regulis Algebrae* he became entitled to a share of the credit for finding a solution of cubic equations such as $x^3 + px = q$, known to science as Cardan's rule.

Mathematics at that time was a constituent part of culture and not such a hermit on the outskirts as it is today, when it seems more like a private reservation for the "happy few." A lively dispute over priority blazed up around the solution of the cubic equation, which Cardan's figures, in spite of all the hard feelings, brought out into the white light of publicity. Tartaglia, the stammerer, whose true name is not known—as a six-year-old boy at the siege of Brescia he had been struck by a French bullet that marred his speech—was a noted teacher of mathematics in Venice and tried to prove that as far back as 1539 he had entrusted to Cardan the secret of the cubic equation hidden in some verses. The true discoverer, however, as history has since determined, was not Tartaglia but Scipione dal Ferro, a professor in Bologna, who in 1505 had revealed it verbally to his friend Antonio Maria Fiore, and he in turn had betrayed it to Tartaglia by the means of appropriate problems. Thus Cardan should have the credit of putting an end to the illegal traffic in this discovery.

Also on the question as to the nature of the process of combustion he forged a link in the centuries-long chain that stretches from Roger Bacon (1260) over endless errors to Lavoisier: he emphasized the necessity of air for combustion. He improved the construction of oil lamps by placing the oil container higher up. He built a meal-sifting machine in which the sifting effect of a current of air was successfully applied, and in 1553 established the fact that lead gains weight when calcined. He was one of the first advocates of blood transfusion, through which, he believed, the morals of criminals could be improved. In 1560 he proved that sound penetrates the bones of the head. He stood with enthusiasm for the study of anatomy.

We see that Cardan was no miracle-worker through whom emotions of the soul or comforts for the body were discovered. He had no kind of banner, no watchword, no shibboleth. And yet his work determined the course of events. His chief books, *De Subtilitate Rerum, Ars Magna, De Varietate Rerum,* mark a turning-point in the development of physical science. After the manner of the great encyclopedias of the Middle Ages they establish the permanence of human knowledge regarding "matter, form, space, motion, the elements, animals, man, the senses, the soul, art and invention, miracles, God, angels and demons."

The significance of Cardan here lies not so much in the brilliance of his achievement as in the ingenious nature of his anthropological methods, which introduced a new era in natural science. A characteristic sort of physiological esthetics in harmony with the time-spirit and style-sense of the Renaissance, turned, through Cardan, the gaze of science to the functions of the human body and the close relations between body and spirit. Thus he becomes an early trail-blazer of psychology.

In his books, *De Subtilitate* and *De Varietate Rerum*

one finds countless aphoristic fragments of this new science: The evil traits of the human race are explained by the mixing of the materials in the body. Sobs and tears are an appropriate means used by nature to break up the physical stoppage created by pain. The appearance of physical changes due to psychic causes is always a worthy object of observation. Harmony and sense-satisfying proportions awaken a feeling of pleasure. In the arrangement of the features of the face, of the parts of a tree, of the columns in a colonnade, the effect of symmetry upon the feelings is demonstrated. Three principles of esthetic effect are set forth: proportion, moderate charm, movement from the less pleasing to the more pleasing impression. A theory of the life spirit is propounded, a hint of which is found in the function of the nervous system: in a state of pleasure the life forces stream outward toward the object, in sadness they are drawn from the outer parts inward, in the case of violently unpleasant emotions suddenly, more slowly when the emotion is constant. These procedures indicate then the changes in the warmth and flow of the blood.* He is constantly busied over the physical bases of his existence: his health, his hold on life, his physical constitution, his native abilities.

Everywhere in Cardan's work one perceives a new

* *De Varietate Rerum*, page 456 et seq.

tone. And however ill-constructed, concealed, and uncertainly formulated the new thought may be, however unbelligerently it may be presented, here is the first place where it sounds forth and out from which it breaks for itself a mighty channel. Cardan is carrying the philosophical battle of the Neo-Platonist against the Aristotelian church scholasticism into the field of natural science.

His opponent is named Galen. To Galen of Pergamos, that gifted and self-willed physician of the second century, had fallen the destiny of being the last doctor of worldwide reputation whose influence still survived at the end of the Roman-culture epoch, six hundred years after Hippocrates. This resultful survival of classic medicine, hardened as it was into dogma and hallowed by the mighty word of the church, remained for more than a thousand years a constant source of new dogmas and a stiff fetter on medieval medicine, which, without creative power of its own, had blindly capitulated to the name behind which the man had vanished, to the authoritarian concept of Galenism, a distorted and dusty degenerate of the doctrine of Hippocrates.

Cardan, in his virile writings, prepared the way for the fall of Galenism. He refuted the idea that catarrh originated in the brain. He denied the universal validity of the principle of Contraria contrariis, and thus be-

came the ancestor of homeopathy and of many modern
scientific views. He held, even then, that water was a
composite substance. "Changes in nature follow the law
of numbers which God has woven into his works.
—All living things have souls: even in plants love and
hate rule.—Man is no animal, but 'all animals,' the sum
of animal life raised to the highest degree." And with
clear, undeniable significance we find in Cardan preliminary traces of the evolutionary theory, spirit of
Lamarck's and Darwin's spirit: "Nature often creates
new species, which again disappear if they cannot main-
tain themselves." *

The abandonment of Galen's system brought the
necessary hypothesis for the rise of modern physical science. Cardan was the intellectual promoter of a revolution whose energies were first hurled like a blazing
torch into the consciousness of men through the vehe-
mence and elementary power and depth of Paracelsus.

Cardan begins to be famous, but the undynamic part
of his being loves to linger in the contemplative and
world-disdaining lethargy of idleness. What he undertakes he does for his family, for posthumous praise, for
the clearing up of his own consciousness: obligations
which an honest man cannot escape. But his true in-

* *De Subtilitate Rerum*, liber XI, Cardano Oper. III. Lugd. 1663. p. 549.

clination is toward the humble, teeming life of the neighborhood in insects and plants.

Again and again he finds himself in the most desirable circumstances, and then, like the plants that clothe themselves or go bare with the changing seasons, he falls ill or lame, or is laden with possessions only to squander them. In 1543 he receives a call to be professor of medicine in the University of Pavia. With that his social standing is for the first time made secure.

Yet even academic life, that most sheltered corner of the intellectual world, was for him bound up with constant unrest. Repeatedly in the twenty years of his professorship at Pavia he had to pack up his great book chests and flee to Milan or hurriedly go and seek a subsistence because no salary could be paid. Soon the professors leave, then the students. But now he is no longer disesteemed and alone as in the years of his great distress. Influential men take pains to help his family, his fame as a physician reaches the governing class, and from Pope Paul III and from the king of Denmark, Christian III, come attractive and honorable invitations to enter their service.

At one stroke Cardan steps into the foremost ranks of earthly glory. Cardinal Alciati, Morone, president of the Council of Trent, and Carlo Borromeo, the saint, protect and advance him. Andreas Vesalius, physician in ordinary to the king and himself king of anatomists, comes into close professional relations with him. The apex of his fame is marked by his journey to Scotland, which he undertook in 1552 to cure Archbishop Hamilton. It gave him a glimpse of the agitated European world, which, stirred from its depths, hesitated before the brilliant internationalism of the humanists, the world that Erasmus had left behind him, under the skies of Copernicus, the power of Michelangelo, the mockery of Aretino, the laughter of Rabelais. A world, also, however, in religious uproar over the grave of Luther, ready to bring fearful blood-sacrifices to the faith. Calvin and Zwingli, the Huguenots, Mary the Catholic in England, this thunderstorm of carnage and cruelty gathered overhead while the powerful hand of Charles V still spasmodically held together that part of the earth.

Cardan traveled through France, England, Holland and Switzerland simply as a physician who treats the body of a patient without regard to his pain or grief. He talked with kings and scholars, but this unpolitical man, well provided for in his strongly held Catholic faith, preferred to study technical matters, the distances between places, the appearance of plants and animals, the influence of climate, and man as "an animal of all animals." In Paris he was fascinated especially by the crown jewels of the French king in the church of St.

Denis—because among them there was a completely preserved horn of a unicorn!

After his return from Edinburgh Cardan lived again for several years in Milan. Now he had no more money troubles, for gifts, honors and honorariums are not withheld from famous physicians. Yet the faster he rose in men's esteem the faster grew the ill-will and detraction that assailed him. Nothing is more provocative and less forgiven than inner freedom. Cardan's distance and isolation, due to the death of his wife and the estrangement from his children, strengthened and concentrated upon himself the hatred of the world. He still had to go through many ordeals of suffering and discouragement. At the end this truth stands out for him: "In general, honor for men is a pitiful thing."

"In the year 1559 Cardan returned to his professorship in Pavia. There the most fearful blow of his life struck him: the death of his son Giambattista." Charged with having poisoned his wife in child-bed, the son was beheaded in prison, April 7, 1560. "That was the harshest and heaviest blow that struck me. . . . From that time forth I went through the streets despised; where I met other people they looked contemptuously over their shoulders; and since I was so unwelcome to them I went out of the way of my friends; I had not the wherewithal to flee. I know not which was the greater, my misery or the hatred with which I was regarded."

Cardan had defended to the uttermost his son, whose guilt or innocence was never clearly proved. After this frightful thing had been inflicted upon him, however, he buried himself in his work and had no social intercourse save with the young students who ventured to live in his house, not without thereby giving new occasion to evil gossip. Thus he held out three years longer in Pavia, then in 1562 accepted a call to Bologna as professor of medicine.

Now sixty years old, Cardan remained, even in this center of academic learning, a hermit turned to stone by care and grief. There lay indeed an aura of veneration about this dark man, eternally grieving, writing and teaching. He was granted the rights of a citizen of honor, he lived in easy circumstances, he dwelt in a column-bedecked palace in the Via San Stefano, and finally in his own house on the little square before the cloister church of San Giovanni in Monte.

The bitterness and iciness of his heart often moved the lonely man to cynicism. "Babblers they are, all of them, skinflints, liars, fighters for glory and power. What mortal could I love? Why, a kitten or a little goat is much cleaner and prettier." His belief in spirits grew ever stronger, a last anchor, since "my tutelary genius is a good and merciful spirit."

Behind the gratings and windows of the lecture room

the invisible spies of the Inquisition were listening; under the arcades of the alleys and streets lurked students, citizens, priests, and the restless social circles of the market-place of learning set wild rumors afloat. Writings went from hand to hand. Warnings were sent to the lonely Cardan, but he was buried behind his folios and never saw them.

On October 13, 1570, fists pounded on his door. Bailiffs hunted the old man out of his sleep and led him away to prison. He was suspected of unbelief and heresy.

For Cardan, now seventy years old, the prison furnishes one of the many dreary landscapes of his life. But what has he to fear who is without hope and who regards it as the highest form of freedom to be alone within four walls?

The imprisoned Cardan showed to his judges the unmilitary courage of humanism, the courage of wisdom and renunciation. The Christian who believed in God and doubted men now bowed to the inquisitors of the Counter-Reformation with the smile of humility that surrendered an ended life and a lost age to foreign quarrels and far-off discord.

"These are the precarious conditions to which you are exposed when you live in a time and a land where the State suffers shipwreck through completely distorted laws. To attempt opposition in this case would be especially difficult, would bring with it anguish and sorrow, and would be thoroughly foolish and futile. Nor would it be less difficult or less dangerous to try to get out of the way of such untoward situations, for the security of all goods and possessions is affected by the public misfortune."

Thanks to the friendly efforts of Cardinals Morone and Carlo Borromeo, Cardan was freed from the clutches of the law. But he had to give up the last remnant of intellectual influence over the world that was so hostile to him: they took away his professorship and forbade him to publish any more of his writings. He signified his willingness, for he was no heretic. At the end of the year 1571 he left Bologna and betook himself to Rome. The Pope granted him a pension on which he could live.

Five years Cardan lived in Rome. Tirelessly he wrote books that dared not appear—wrote them as if they were to be published. He trusted to the power of the written word, which is stronger and more lasting than the created body. Once again he set in order the events of his life and gave us the now famous account of his career, a painfully temperate, incorruptibly true encyclopedia of the sorrows and joys of a peaceful man in a restless age. Whatever of manly restraint in sorrow and anguish, whatever of lasting good this unpathetic sinner and repenter had accomplished in the way of magnificently organizing and interpreting living nature, that book was to show.

Cardan died on September 20, 1576, and was buried at San Marco in Milan beside his father.

ANDREAS VESALIUS

The Founder of Anatomy

II

ANDREAS VESALIUS

The Founder of Anatomy

WE ALL know the type of the overworked, tired, disillusioned physician, deadened by routine. Perhaps we are that kind ourselves in moments of disappointment or loss of faith, heathen of the healing art, skeptically or cynically cut off from the old faith in the inward call of our calling. These despondent doctors are not the bad doctors, for the averting of death and the comforting of sorrow and pain are entrusted to weak powers. To such discouraged members of the profession we would recommend an experience which is too generally neglected, but which it is never too late to obtain: They should leave their patients for an hour (if they live in Berlin), go to the State Library, and draw from that stone dungeon of the spirit a book by Andreas Vesalius, *De Humani Corporis Fabrica,* printed at Basel in the office of Johannes Oporinus in the year of our Lord 1543.

Over this book a physician can only rave like a poet

over the view of an overpowering landscape, so decisive
is its impress upon his emotions, and so lasting and
decisive its significance for the value of his own life.
For the doctor of today usually lacks perspective;
he gets his knowledge from the latest editions of the
textbooks, and anything "out of date" fills him with
honest contempt. He does not notice, when as a
student he consults the latest revised edition of Rauber-
Kopsch or the fine volumes of Brauss on Anatomy
(devoted to the greater names in the medical fraternity), that the name of Vesalius is not to be found
therein. He does not suspect that this insignificant-
looking symptom of disdain for the past is killing
his career at the root. The anatomy book of today
is a useless catalog of technical names, while the
anatomy book of Vesalius is a textbook of passionate
devotion to medicine. Any doctor who has made the
acquaintance of this book, the work of a young man
of twenty-eight, will love his calling and all through
life will realize its deep and dangerous beauty.

De Humani Corporis Fabrica is a work of art that,
in the rounded unity of its type, illustrations, format
and letterpress, takes rank beside the great and unique
creations of the early printers of religious books. It is
not too much to say that essentially it belongs in the
same category, and that only through a consciousness

of the divine nature of the human body could it have grown to such greatness.

The frontispiece of this imposing folio volume, whose back is strengthened with the remains of a parchment incunabulum, staggers the beholder at first glance today. Here, in all its details, is the last public demonstration in anatomy given by Vesalius in 1543. In the middle of the page he stands, at the dissecting table, on which lies a woman's body with the entrails visible in the opening that has been made in it. At the head of this corpse rises an accusing skeleton with uptilted skull, done with the allegorical power and positive infallibility that radiate in almost uncanny fashion from every illustration in this book. In the foreground two squatting barbers are whetting their razors, while an almost countless throng of figures—standing, sitting on benches, looking down from the seats of the anatomical theater—surrounds the event with the drawn faces of men trembling with excitement and perplexity. The ape and the dog, hitherto the subjects of dissection, flank the picture, and on the right, climbing upon a column, is a naked man who well may serve for observation of the play of living muscles. High above this human swarm, almost secondary to it, appears the title of the work framed with a human-superhuman bearded face and the caricatures of two apes; and still above that is poised the coat of arms of Vesalius—three fleeing weasels.

As an artistic achievement the page could not take supreme rank, but it gives so convincing and immediate an impression of the stirring event that we are carried along irresistibly by the significance of the moment, and suspect that what is happening here is to change the world in astonishing and undreamed-of measure. Anatomy, the foundation-stone of medical science and of the whole science of the human body, is being created before our eyes. The body, the soul's house, is being explored and appraised in all its nooks and crannies, all its depths and currents, and now for the first time the picture of the earth is complete. The most unknown, the most unapproachable, the most forbidden island is discovered. How this marvel of re-creating the human body, which falls to the lot of every medical student, has been degraded for us, becoming a mere pedantic exercise! How the first painful and shrinking familiarities with the dead have been dishonored and robbed of their thrill!

On the broad pages of Vesalius anatomy remains, even in the most minute and exhaustive consideration of a small bone, the fountain-head of the science of life, a thing of devotion and culture. At the same time, however, the book is a stormy voyage of discovery, comparable only to the achievement of Columbus, a daring enterprise well prepared for and sure of its purpose.

The title page likewise proclaims the revolutionary change in anatomical research. There for the first time stands the youthful professor among his students, beside the body, with the knife and chisel in his own hand. The centuries-old customs of the anatomical theater are shattered. For hitherto a strict three-part system has persisted, such as we find preserved today in the old wooden-tabled Teatro Anatomico in Bologna, the classic abode of the first dissections of the human body. How difficult it must have been to break through such a system congealed into architecture!

High above, on a sort of throne, the professor sat and read aloud, without looking up, a chapter of Galen or Mondino. A little lower, but also still raised, stood the demonstrator, a physician, and pointed with a wooden staff at the organs to which the reading referred. Then, far below, in the depths with the gruesome object of study, were barbers, the executioners of anatomy, cutting up the body or rather mangling it with rude, unpractised hands. It was regarded as highly indecent for a professor to take the knife in his hand. The physicians themselves were divided into the separate hierarchies of medical doctors and surgeons. Any infringement of the boundary line was a flagrant offense against professional honor.

As a student in Paris Vesalius had suffered under these conditions. Of his teacher, Guenther von Andernach—a philological devotee who used his eyes, with which he should have been seeing, to write himself blind on translations of Galen—he reports that he never saw him with a knife in his hand except at the dinner table. Much more dangerous, however, because more corrupt, was the figure of another teacher, Jacques Dubois, who went under the literary name of Sylvius, and at whose feet gathered more than four hundred knowledge-hungry physicians from all over Europe.

Sylvius united elegance with a pampered mind, the pleasing form of a humanist culture with the narrowness of a reactionary brain. A brain that would not tolerate the slightest change in his ideas, delivered over, body and soul, to the doctrines of Galen. Later, when Vesalius came out as a heretic regarding Galenism, Sylvius also lost completely his humanistic style and launched forth into wild abuse of this former pupil who once had been his pride.

Vesalius possessed at his birth in Brussels, December 31, 1514, the priceless heritage of generations of scientific tradition. His early maturity and his incorruptible,

inborn scientific and artistic feeling for style, in union
with his youthful activity, helped to bring his great
book to happy completion. Not without cause does his
family's coat of arms refer with pride to this epoch-
making work.

The ancestors of Vesalius called themselves Witing
and hailed from Wesel in Prussia. Then the family
moved to Nymwegen and took the name of Wessele or
Vesalius. His great-great-grandfather Peter had written
a treatise on the "medical law book" of Avicenna, the
great Arabian physician Ibn Sina, who lived about the
year 1000, and whose fame blinded the eyes of medieval
science perhaps even more than that of Galen. His
great-grandfather John was a professor at Louvain,
physician in ordinary to Maximilian I and Mary of
Burgundy. From that time forth the men of the Vesalius family remained medical confessors of the ruling
house of Burgundy and Austria. The grandfather,
Eberhard, wrote a commentary on the famous ninth
section of the medical treatise dedicated to Prince
Almansor by the esteemed physician Ar-Rhati or
Rhazes, one of the greatest clinical experts of the Middle
Ages. This manuscript of his grandfather served as the
basis of the first-born work of Vesalius, which he
brought out at Louvain in February, 1537—a standard
new translation of the ninth book of Almansor, which

retained lasting value for its clinical analysis of Arabic and Galenic medicine.

Vesalius's father was druggist in ordinary to Charles V and his constant companion on the numerous campaigns and diplomatic journeys of the emperor. Meanwhile his mother, Isabella Crabbe, took care of the young Andreas, showed him the manuscripts and books of his ancestors, and directed his first steps on the road to fame. When in his studies he came to the structure of the walls of the veins, he remembered the fibrous markings on the bladders that in boyhood had been attached to him while learning to swim. He led the life of a young Asclepiad. He began early to ask himself questions, and he found the answers himself. He lost his shyness before the things of nature and kept up his enthusiasm. This serious problem of education was brilliantly solved in his case and received grateful recognition in the fascinating initials of his anatomical book, upon which little, chubby, cheerful boys, the angels of anatomy, are performing the gruesome task of dissection in cheerful and sportive fashion.

To have overcome the horror connected with the decaying material, not by means of unreality but by means of art—that is the wonderful achievement of Vesalius. Through him death becomes a going forward of life, dying a creative act. His skeletons are celestial beings with human outlines, creatures of the highest psychical expression and intellectual power. Their suffering or grieving forms keep rising continually out of the subsoil of an animated landscape. The lay figures shed their muscles on all sides like a tall, blooming tree, and the landscape suffers and lives with them. The series is filled with dramatic suspense; on bare, naked rock they stand now, until at last, robbed of every hold and connection, the poor human remnants, breaking down, lean against a wall or sink on their knees, or, martyred, are drawn upward by cords.

What Vesalius is here describing and getting an artist to depict, doubtless under his exact directions, is the complete vision of the years of his youth. Presumably the artist who did it was his friend on the lower Rhine, Johann Stephan von Calkar, a pupil of Titian whom he had first engaged in Padua for his work.

The childhood passion for seeing the inside of things, for opening, for pulling apart and thus at last possessing, has by no means died down in him. The play of the boy becomes the calling of the man. The boy dissects mice, moles, rats, dogs, and cats, and what he then discovers in the delicate, disorderly, puzzling confusion of the entrails takes away the nausea of the smell and feel of what he is handling. He is early aware that death is the only certainty, a settled thing between God and man, but what he uncovers is a world in itself, a mirroring of heaven, a department of the cosmic order and everlastingness, like the universe. And without a qualm he forces his way into the secret of this order, which is blood of his blood and flesh of his flesh.

His college education, his knowledge of Latin, Greek and Hebrew, with the elements of dialectics, arithmetic and astronomy, Vesalius obtained in the celebrated schools of Louvain.

In 1533 he went as a student to Paris, in his pocket a definite plan of study given to him by his father's friend, Court Physician Nicolas Florenas, to whom he gratefully dedicated his first book. Vesalius means to be a physician.

Paris at that time was the headquarters of Neo-Galenism. The city of fashion was vehemently giving the death blow to Arabian medicine. Avicenna was done for. Everybody who was anybody swore by the westerner, Galen, after the fiery battle of Pierre Brissot for certain innovations in the bloodletting method was decided in his favor. The Arabians advocated bleeding on the side opposite to the inflammation, whereas Hippocrates ordered it on the afflicted side. The strife between the revulsionists and the derivativists took on such violent and disturbing proportions that the emperor had to take a hand and designate the University of Salamanca as the final judge between them. This authority decided for Hippocrates and his high priest, Galen. To establish the Galen cult upon the sure foundation of humanism now became the object of the ruling class of intellectuals. The leaders of this group were Sylvius and Guenther, who, as we have seen, were the medical teachers of Vesalius.

Teachers whom he soon learned to despise. For the bodies of dogs which, hacked up by the barbers, were exhibited now and then in the college, or the annual dissection of a human cadaver which became a show for low-minded citizens with broad backs that completely blocked the view of the students, deeply wounded the passionate earnestness of the young scientist. Never did he see a nerve, an artery, a vein, never dared he take a bone in his hand.

So he undertook to help himself, and roamed all day through the churchyards and places of execution. At St. Innocent and at the gallows of Montfaucon he was a constant visitor, a desperate treasure seeker looking for bones and wild dogs, whom he robbed of their booty and killed with stones, then dragged home in order to dissect them carefully in the peace and quiet of his room. Once he and a friend were almost torn to pieces by the savage animals.

Soon he had made such progress that he could recognize every bone with closed eyes by touching it. His exceptional ability was swiftly noised abroad. He was awarded the honor of taking over the rôle of the barber at demonstrations, and Guinterius consulted him in the writing of his *Institutiones Anatomacae,* a widely circulated summary of Galen's system of anatomy.

He was filled with anger and disillusionment, however, by the unscrupulous way in which his teachers suppressed and distorted everything that conflicted with their theories. He swore that he would wake anatomy from the dead, making it better than ever before, or at least that he would make it possible some day to compare his method of dissection with the classical method without blushing. "Nothing in our time has fallen so low and been so completely restored at one stroke as anatomy."

The idea held him spellbound and drove him beyond the bounds of reason and good breeding. He held the beating heart of an executed criminal in his hand, the bleeding head of one decapitated. He locked himself in with his dead bodies, robbed the gallows by night, macerated and cooked the bones, smuggled them one at a time into his quarters, and built there from countless discarded parts the magnificently shameless framework of the human body.

The Parisian student period of Vesalius came to a sudden end. Duke Francesco Sforza of Milan had died in 1536. Francis I of France regarded himself as successor to the control of Milan, and, having allied himself with Suleiman II against Charles V, was now advancing on Paris with his army from Italy. Doubtless Vesalius's father was in the army before which the son took flight, returning to Louvain.

The young doctor was admitted to the long, beautiful hall of the cloth merchants, in which, after the decline of the business, Pope Martin V for more than a hundred years housed the university, already renowned for its courses in anatomy. He had scarcely more than arrived before he had to undertake the dissection of an eighteen-year-old girl who had died under circumstances involving suspicion of poisoning. Already both famous and infamous, he found many friends and many enemies. He got the porter to let him out at night and procured from the gallows the finest skeleton he had ever seen; it lacked only the fingers of one hand, the knee caps, and one foot. He dissected it by the pale light of the moon and smuggled it, bit by bit, into the city by secret ways.

Soon the students saw a bold marvel: after eighteen years a public lesson in anatomy was given again in Louvain. Young Vesalius, one of themselves, dissected and taught at the same time. The insurmountable professorial lecture-table seemed to be overthrown. This dissection in Louvain was one of the young doctor's most dangerous adventures. To the professors of theology he became both annoying and sinister. The future annihilator of Galen was suspected by the fanatical Arabists of Louvain of being a protestant Galenist, a Luther of medicine. Thus do dogmas allow themselves to be pressed into every form; they are not rigid, as men suppose, but plastic yet impenetrable. For Vesalius the discussions with the provincial professors of Louvain—the hateful strife over bloodletting on the right or left side, the philosophical wrangling over classical and Arabic medicine—were a sad example of the academic inferiority that pursued him all his life, and in which the glowering visage of the Inquisition played a dangerous rôle.

Everybody around Vesalius talked himself blind. Galen and Avicenna were suffering a bitter fate: over their great achievements doctrinal gravestones were rising high. Doctrines meant hatred, falsification, misunderstanding. Vesalius, concerned with his own intellectual progress, and startled by so much senseless outcry and wrangling, laid aside the classical writings, which he already knew very well.

With a sure instinct he fled from Louvain into a sphere where a genuine battle of intellects was under way. At the beginning of 1537 he was in Venice.

Venice at that time was the focus of Catholic self-searching. A crusade of humility, of devotion, of weaponless resistance to an immoral and diseased society had begun. Luxury and pestilence, culture and stenches, beauty and syphilis, the serenity of the Greek gods, the opulence of the unexpectedly widened world and groans of hunger: thus the Renaissance seemed to be drawing to a somber close. Venice was the glory and the sinkhole of that time. Suddenly there arose in it this powerful crusade of brotherly love, fairly unexampled in history. Around the Benedictine abbot, Cortese; around the already-founded order of Theatins and its leader, Gianpietro Caraffa, later Pope Paul IV; and, most of all, around the first ragged and self-sacrificing companions of Ignatius Loyola, the Spanish aristocrat, also once a student at Paris, who through self-abasement and mire rose to lordly power, there was gathering an ever-increasing congregation.

Ignatius and his first Jesuits cared for the dying, the prisoners, the lepers in their holes; they made their way into the hospitals for a raid on dirt and refuse; they washed, scoured and scrubbed, they knew no disgust when they had to deal with vermin, pus and filth. For the first time in a long dark age the voice of God spoke to hard hearts, the churches became again places of devotion, and man, that dull lump of misery, could weep once more over misfortune or happiness.

This onset destroyed the walls between science and

everyday life. Vesalius, who, as was customary, had visited no patients during his studies, found himself gripped by the breath of illness and its terrible needs. He took hold, bled patients, set leeches to work, shrank not from the handclasp of the lowly barber. He was one of the first to test the wonderful healing powers of quinine, which sailors had brought over from Peru. In that same year he went to Padua. On December 5 he passed the examination for his doctor's degree, and the very next day, at the age of twenty-two, he began his teaching work as professor of surgery and anatomy.

Through his swift and sure rise, Vesalius has now attained a station which gives him the means to realize the dream of his life—the renovation of anatomy. He begins at once with a thorough reorganization of anatomical instruction. With hitherto unheard-of thoroughness he prepares beforehand for each public dissection. Hundreds of physicians, philosophers, theologians, come streaming in to hear every word of his demonstrations, which continue tirelessly each forenoon and afternoon for three long weeks. He urges the judges not to execute a sentence at the wrong time and not to make use of any mutilating form of death. In a short time a complete skeleton is set up. Dissection of dogs and other animals accompanies his lectures.

Straightway these first attempts at comparative anatomy play an important part in deciding the trend of his further researches. Galen is still his recognized model; even though many a doubt may assail him secretly, Galen's work on bones is still almost wholly accepted. But he now detects the first considerable errors of Galen. The course of the so-called azygous vein, which lies in the chest along the spine, is entirely different from Galen's description of it; and this fact leads Vesalius, who does a great deal of bloodletting, to an entirely new method of procedure, which he publishes in 1539 in his *Letter on Bloodletting*. Intuitiveness and exactness are his supreme rules. While this is still in press he draws up schematic outlines covering the whole subject, and soon his students hold in their hands the *Tabulae Anatomicae* promised to them in the first lecture.

With every dissection his knowledge and certainty are deepened. He is far more the leader of an exploring expedition into an unknown land than the superior commentator on established facts. This consciousness of being eye-witnesses of new and unheard-of discoveries creates the dramatic suspense that grips his hearers.

It is most fascinating to study the first anatomical publications of Vesalius. Three papers—on the arterial system, the venous system, and the aorta with heart and kidneys—are signed by him; three others bear the skeleton signature of Johann Stephan von Calcar, the

artist who from now on became his tireless fellow
worker. He emphasizes in the text that not a line
in the pictures is contrary to nature; everything is just
as he had shown it to his spectators in Padua. But if
one examines carefully, one encounters a noteworthy
example of the intellectual blindness which a prevailing
idea imposes upon even the most gifted observer: The
liver still is shown with five lobes, the breastbone still
consists of seven parts, the womb is shaped like a bubble,
the heart is wrongly sketched, the pelvis falsely situated,
though in other outstanding cases the correction of
Galen has begun.

The anatomical obsession of Vesalius rose with every
deepening of his knowledge. In the years 1539 and
1540 he was called from Padua to Bologna. In the
classic haunts of the foremost university, where the first
human dissections on Italian soil had been made, he
carried through the first sensation-creating demonstrations of the sources of error in Galenic anatomy. In
five years at Padua he had succeeded in dissecting six
female bodies, in one of which he found, for the first
time, anatomical proof of the hymen. Ceaselessly he
observed himself, his friends, his pupils, the viands
that were served to him. He was the first scientific observer of human birth. He spent hours at the butcher
shop, because a physician could learn more there than
in the usual public demonstrations. From the locksmith

he learned how to rivet together a skeleton, from the weaver, comb-maker and goldsmith how to repair instruments effectively. There was no portion of his whole day that he did not devote to his profession.

With the year 1540 Vesalius was approaching the knowledge that was to be decisive of his destiny. The book publisher Giunta in Venice was planning a reliable Latin edition of Galen's collected works. This ambitious undertaking aimed to make a living form out of the phantom Galen, who for many physicians remained only a hazy concept because of their ignorance of Greek; but it required an enormous sacrifice of money and labor. Giunta died under it, but his heirs went on pushing the work and devoted their fortune to it. A feverish search went on all over Italy for manuscripts and texts. The most famous and highly educated men in the country worked gratis for this sacred cause. The proofreading expert, Galdadinus, fell seriously ill from excitement and overwork. The editor was the most celebrated Galenist of his time, Giambattista Montanus of Verona, a friend of Vesalius. In 1541 this magnificent, handsomely bound Venetian Galen came from the press.

Vesalius had undertaken to work over the text dealing with the dissection of the nerves and vascular system, and especially Galen's most important volume, *De Anatomicis Administrationibus*. And now at last he saw with certainty, in the course of his strenuous critical labors, what he had hitherto dimly sensed and had not dared to confess to himself: Galen's anatomy was patchwork, full of misinterpretations and errors!

While he was doing this work of translation he was delivering his second course of anatomy lectures in Bologna. For Professor Albius, whose guest he was, he completed the skeleton of a man and one of a monkey. When the work was finished, he tested it by comparing the two skeletons. In that of the monkey he found a lumbar vertebral process which was in Galen's anatomy, but which he had sought in vain in the human skeleton.

That day of the year 1540 was the birthday of modern anatomy. Vesalius now knew that Galen had never dissected a human body! His anatomy was that of the ape. Everything still remained to be done! The innumerable obscurities and wrong ideas that had bothered him were cleared up at one stroke. The years of desperate search for the papery organs mentioned by Galen were at an end; the feeling of incompetence that assailed him when he could not find in man the Plexus mirabilis so minutely described, though he did find it in sheep; the anxiety lest he be accused of ignorance or stupidity when he saw things differently from the infallible Galen.

Now he understood Galen's dark reference to the

skeleton that he had seen in Alexandria. It was the astonishment of awe for the deep learning of the Alexandrian school, for the vast, almost trackless past when Herophilus and Eristratus still dared to dissect human bodies methodically in the Museum and Serapeum, and, what is more, as Celsus tells us, to cut living criminals to pieces for purposes of study. Galen's time no longer knew human anatomy! Again and again he refers to the far-reaching similarity between the anatomy of man and that of the monkey. The position of the surface veins in the arm of a living man is exactly like that of the dead ape; hence, Galen concludes, it is certain that the inside of the animal and the inside of a man are exactly alike.

The reaction of Vesalius to his astonishing discovery was surprising: he was ashamed of himself. One sees how far the new spirit of humility, the spirit of Loyola, had removed him from the ethics of that passion for glory which ruled the Renaissance. "I could not get through wondering at my own stupidity and overconfidence in Galen and the writings of other anatomists."

The motto of Vesalius was the slogan of the Asclepiads regarding the duty of the physician: "Ocyus, jucunde et tuto"—"Swift, good-humored and sure." We find it under his portrait on the first page of the *Fabrica*. Without hesitating he went to work to describe the anatomy of man for the first time—so long as the world shall stand, the true, ungarbled facts about the make-up of the human body!

This enormous task Vesalius mastered in two years. Still more difficult, however, than this triumphant conquest of the human body, was the deposing of Galen from his place in public opinion. This was a world-historic act of destruction and construction, a wild battle between progress and the irrational powers of conservatism. The last public dissections in Padua were like excited mobs. Stormy objections, stormy applause greeted him when he hurled Galen from the pedestal of divinity by citing more than two hundred of Galen's errors. "Thou Galenist, who hast been betrayed by thine apes!" Thus he reproached himself. But the doubters and mockers aimed their poison at him.

On August 1, 1542, his work was completed. He took it to Venice and allowed the enormous manuscript, with all the woodcuts, directions to the printer, and very definite requests, all carefully packed, to be sent through the business house of Danoni to his publisher, Oporinus, in Basel, with the remark that he would oversee the printing himself.

Vesalius was twenty-eight years old. In the wood-cut portrait at the beginning of his book on anatomy, of which we have already spoken, we see his bold seafarer's face, framed in crisp hair, a swelling and heavy brow, an uptilted nose, a small birthmark over the right eyebrow; but, above all, we notice the eyes, which penetrate the beholder and convince him at one glance that this self-confident, efficient man, in good or evil, has something extraordinary to show us. The hands of Vesalius are busy upon an anatomical subject. One sees the half of a dead body in an upright position, and the flexor muscles of the right forearm are laid bare. Vesalius is grasping this inexorable proof of something which Galen had misrepresented and which he understands. A freshly written paper lying on the dissecting table transfixes Galen's misstatement and pronounces judgment upon it.

At the beginning of the year 1543 Vesalius is received in Basel with all academic honors. He is not sorry to take the broad road into the city of the famous book publisher. Under his eyes the work grows from day to day. Nor is he idle in other ways. On May 12, 1543, Jacob Karrer of Gebweiler is beheaded. Vesalius performs the first dissection that has taken place in Basel in twelve years, and from the bones of the convict constructs a skeleton that outlasts the unknown misdeeds of Jacob Karrer for centuries; for today it is still treasured by the Vesalius Museum in Basel as the oldest preserved piece of anatomical work in the world.

His book appeared in June, 1543. Actually it was two books. For, besides the creative and exhaustive masterpiece, the *Fabrica,* there appeared at the same time the *Epitome,* an extract for laymen, a review of the new doctrine, a safeguard against plagiarists and reprinters, in both a Latin and a German edition ("Concerning the Anatomy of the Human Body: A Brief but Extremely Useful Summary. . . . Interpreted by D. Albanus Torinus for the Benefit of the Ordinary Reader"). Thus the organization of Vesalius's work was carried out most completely and carefully. Where contradictions to traditional ideas appeared—and this occurred on almost every page—the changes were discussed to the minutest details; not only were the errors traced, but also their psychological, historical and logical sources. The style of the treatise, which happily has to make use only of facts as weapons, is one of striking superiority.

But the slime which every wave stirs up did not fail to appear forthwith. It showed up first on the spot. His pupil and substitute, Realdo Colombo, who later became physician in ordinary to Paul IV, an unscrupulous and gifted place hunter, took the first opportunity in Padua to make his teacher Vesalius an object of scorn and laughter for the whole world. Like a field marshal Vesalius dashed by forced marches to the threatened front. At the end of 1543 he appeared in Padua—to the confusion of Colombo—and settled accounts with his opponent in a brilliantly conducted public dissection.

The rise of the young physician gave no rest to the envious, however. Abusive letters by the distinguished old Nicholas Massa, attacking the tyro Vesalius, were circulated in Padua. On every corner somebody was trying to set fire to his great work. His bitterest and most dangerous enemy was his old teacher, Sylvius. With really pathological hatred, both by voice and by written word, he pursued the heretic Vesalius throughout many years. He called him a madman, a cursed mocker, nicknamed him "a certain Vesanus," and denounced him as a crude and ignorant upstart who could do nothing but disgrace his teacher. All the opposition arguments of Sylvius were aimed at the "false doctrine of the physical degeneration of man." If meniscuses are now present in our joints, he argued, they were absent in ancient times, because Galen did not describe them; therefore man must have changed, since Galen was infallible.

While Vesalius was traveling to the reopened University of Pisa, in order to conduct a dissection there at the invitation of Duke Cosimo de Medicis, he paused in Bologna to revisit his friends. But the detractions and agitations against him were becoming constantly worse, especially as they were now reaching the hitherto friendly Charles V, who shortly before had offered him a place as court physician.

After such superhuman labors and iron endurance it

looks almost like a revolt of the nerves, a collapse before the sudden emptiness of his life, when in an hour of doubt he threw into the fire the greater part of his scientific materials. He destroyed his notes on Galenic anatomy, his personal, annotated copy of Galen, and his commentaries on Rhazes. He went farther than that: he abandoned his whole past life, this life of research in the neighborhood of decay. He fled from the distorted faces of the dead, from the silence, from the intolerable, crumbling world where suffering was no longer possible.

Vesalius began his career as court physician to his majesty Charles V at Madrid in 1544. He married Anna von Hamme, the daughter of an esteemed royal councilor in Brussels, and they had a child. He was in a new and different world.

Was he lured by the task of becoming the physician of the most difficult patient? Was it inherited instinct that made him take the road of his fathers? Was it the secret longing to be like other people, the depressing effect of knowledge, this persecution of the researcher that continually pursued him?

Twenty years of court life lay before Vesalius. Charles V had a badly degenerated constitution. His mother was diseased in mind. As a youth he suffered from epileptic attacks. He was early subject to severe pains in the joints, and to these were soon added asthmatic troubles and digestive disturbances. He was a domineering, self-willed patient, and belonged, as Vesalius wrote, "to the princes who wish to be rulers in medicine as well."

It was an enormous leap for Vesalius from his sovereign realm of shadows into answering for the most costly life in Europe. He accompanied the emperor through wars and conferences. We find him in Nymwegen, the old home of his family; in Brussels, in the Reichstag at Regensburg. While here he recommends Cardan as physician in ordinary to the king of Denmark and addresses to his friend Joachim Roelants, city physician of Mechelen, the celebrated *Letter on Quinine,* which finally makes its appearance in print in Ferrara.

This letter ends in an angry outcry against his calumniators and an abrupt renunciation of the life of an investigator:

"Never again will I procure subjects of dissection for myself and my pupils with such labor and danger as once I did in Paris, Louvain, and in Italy, keeping them in my room a week at a time and allowing myself to be martyred by artists. In my youthful enthusiasm for science I endured this willingly and easily. Now I am through with the craze for writing books. My notes on

Galen and many others besides have gone into the fire!"

In the Reichstag at Augsburg, whither he accompanied the emperor, he worked on the second edition of the *Fabrica,* which appeared between 1552 and 1555. The year 1551 had found him making a difficult journey across the Tirolese Mountains with his royal master, who was very ill of the gout. In the winter he lay before Metz. The health of Charles V, however, was becoming ever more critical. Even in Titian's painting of the battle of Mühlberg (1548) he is holding himself on his horse with difficulty, stark and stiff with crabbed energy, and held together only by his iron coat of mail.

There follow years of rest for Vesalius. In Brussels he occupies a roomy house on the Haute Rue. His reputation as a physician is still growing, with deep awe for his traditional second sight. In 1555 he is called to attend the Augsburg patrician Leonhard Welser, in whom he diagnoses an aneurism of the aorta, a dilatation of the great artery, which after two years is confirmed by dissection. He is the first doctor to recognize this serious ailment in a living person, and he remains the only one for a long time. Morgagni, the great pathological anatomist of the eighteenth century, calls the diagnosis of Vesalius "at that time marvelous and unrivaled."

The life of Vesalius took a new turn in 1556. Charles V abdicated and gave over his throne to his son Philip II. With a few loyal followers he withdrew for the rest of his life into the solitude of the Spanish cloister of San Juste. Vesalius went immediately into the service of Philip.

Out of that period probably comes the portrait of Vesalius ascribed to Titian, which today is still to be seen in the Palazzo at Florence. It produces so strange an impression that its identity is often doubted. And yet, for one who understands how to follow up the changes of the human countenance, it contains the staggering power of reality.

Of the powerfully compact form of the young Vesalius nothing remains but the frame of hair about the face. The brow is the brow of Vesalius, but the broad, pale brow of a man growing old. The beard is a graying, slightly ruffled fur that melts into the enormous breadth of the thickening body. The right hand holds the spectacles, the left holds a book with the index finger between its pages, and the wise, resigned, sad eyes sweep in dreamy, thoughtful quietness past the beholder into melancholy-filled space.

Such must have been the appearance of Vesalius when, after the volcanic birth of his great intellectual achievements, he wandered out into the beckoning domains of human activity with their promise of happiness. He is leaving the ascetic world of the dead, in which he has founded a kingdom of clarity and order, to be a sympathizing physician in the agitated confusion of the living, active-blooded world of human passions. It is Vesalius without ideas, Vesalius without weapons, in the depths of discouragement, Vesalius in the shadow of the Spanish darkness, in the empire of Philip II, where the sun never rises, and where he must fail and sink.

Still in the employ of Philip, Vesalius takes up his residence in 1559 at the royal court in the Netherlands. Here he receives the manuscript of Gabriele Falloppio's *Observationes Anatomicae,* which stirs in him a last impulse of research.

Falloppio of Modena had an early career much like that of Vesalius. At twenty-four he was a professor in Ferrara, and he succeeded to Vesalius's chair in the University of Padua after the departure of the faithless Colombo. In his clear, forthright script, every line of which breathes the deepest respect for the founder of anatomy, he advises Vesalius of a few errors, describes the organs of hearing, and gives an admirable account of the uterus, the ovaries, the clitoris. He is the first to explore the evolutionary history of the bones and teeth.

For Vesalius this whole manuscript is a trumpet-call out of a forgotten world—out of his world, in which his happiness lies buried and which without him is continuing to grow and burst into new bloom. He reads as in a fever, as in a fever he sits him down and throws off in a few days his last work, the reply to Falloppio, in which he greets the younger generation, although Falloppio is only nine years younger than Vesalius. It is the greeting of one who has grown prematurely old to one doomed to an early death. For when the Venetian ambassador, Tiepolo, tries to deliver this manuscript to him in 1562, Falloppio is dead at the age of thirty-nine. Two years later the book is published in Venice.

The last book of Vesalius shows a tragic weakness. The seeker for truth has become the scholar of the pen, which he had once so hated; a helpless pedagog of his own doctrine, the tools for which had been struck from his hand, since in all Spain, with its flaming funeral pyres of the Inquisition, there was no human skull on which Vesalius dared to experiment.

Filled with a measureless longing, Vesalius sets forth early in 1564 on his last journey, sees Italy once more, "foster mother of the spirit," meets in the bookstores of Venice his old friend Galdadinus, publisher of the Venetian edition of Galen, and then embarks on the sea voyage from which he is never to return.

The death of Vesalius at the age of fifty upon his pilgrimage to Jerusalem is veiled in impenetrable darkness. Certain absolutely contradictory traditions have come down to us. On January 1, 1565, Dr. Hubert Languetus of Paris writes to Dr. Caspar Peucer, Melanchthon's counselor, what he has learned.

"They say that Vesalius is dead. As you are aware, he was traveling to Jerusalem—going for a strange reason, as some one has written us from Spain. A distinguished patient was entrusted to his care, but the nature of the man's illness was not clear to him. When he believed him dead, he asked the relatives for permission to perform an autopsy. This was granted, but when he cut a hole in the chest, the heart was still beating.

"The relatives complained to the Inquisition, accusing Vesalius of manslaughter and godlessness. Since the killing was proved, the Inquisition would sentence him to death. Only with difficulty was the king able, by reason of his position, or rather by means of his entreaties, to free him from great danger. Finally he was released on condition that for the expiation of his sin he should go on a pilgrimage to Jerusalem and Mount Sinai."

On his return journey, according to another report, he was driven by a storm upon the island of Zante, where he lay ill and forsaken, because the residents thought he was a victim of the plague. A Venetian goldsmith, this story adds, chanced to find him on the beach and cared for and buried him.

These explanations throw no light on the secret of the death of Vesalius. No one knows whether he, like his great opponent Galen, or like his imperial master Charles V, intentionally let himself fall from the heights; whether he thought to go the way of Ignatius, whether he wished to expiate a sin or fared forth in order somewhere at last to find his home. No man was with him, and no man heard his last word. No Asclepiad can play with his bones.

On the tomb upon which the figure of Death in the *Fabrica* thoughtfully leans, Vesalius has chiseled the words: "Vivitur ingenio, caetera mortis erunt"—"One lives for the spirit, all else belongs to Death."

When one closes the deathless work of Andreas Vesalius, *De Humani Corporis Fabrica,* one finds on the last page the imprint-colophon of Oporinus, which is said to have been selected by Vesalius. Arion, the poet and musician of Lesbos, when robbed and thrown into the sea by Corinthian sailors during a voyage, is said by the sweetness of his tones to have called to his aid a dolphin, which took him on its back and carried him to land. In the picture one sees the bard, his instrument in his hand, just reaching the island of rescue.

Around the sketch are the words, "Invia virtuti nulla est via"—"For the man of courage, no way is closed."

Thus did the great and intimate friend of death, with a presentiment of his fate, establish his own memorial.

MICHAEL SERVETUS

Discoverer of the Minor Circulation of the Blood

III

MICHAEL SERVETUS

Discoverer of the Minor Circulation of the Blood

ON THE left bank of the Rhone near Geneva, in the suburbs of the hill town of Champel, there lies hidden between the walls of the Canton Hospital and a villa garden the little Rue Michel Servète, at whose lower end stands a granite block with an inscription to the man for whom the street is named.

Who was Servetus?

On the morning of October 27, 1553, the key grated for the last time in the heavy door and he was taken out of the dark hole in which for months he had languished and moldered. A police officer and a government official ordered him to follow them. When he emerged from the door of the prison, there stood Farel, the old man who for twenty years had burned images of the saints, stormed the cloisters, overcome the church, and "in the spirit of the gospel" had established a theocracy in his home city upon the ruins of "popery." Against a corrupt clergy and the tyrannous oppression

67

of the Dukes of Savoy, Farel had stirred up a passion of national pride and religious reform. To his cry of freedom and reform came a response from Calvin, a refugee out of France and the gloomiest messenger of God that ever lived—the man who stifled in long martyrdom the laughter which Geneva still lacks today.

The prisoner's dour companions led him in silence to the door of the courthouse, from whose balcony the sentence against Michael Servetus, a native of Villanueva in the Spanish kingdom of Aragon, was read. It was an endlessly long catalog of sins and devilish heresies and general God-forsakenness, and the ragged Servetus, blinded by the unaccustomed light of day and stunned by the city's noises, stared with the painful intensity of a man hard of hearing at the form which was spitting forth the flood of his sins, sentence upon sentence. At last, however, the accuser came to the closing words:

"We, councilors and judges of this city, Michael Servetus, have brought action against you, through which it is established that you have written and distributed books against God the Father, Son, and Holy Ghost, and have sought to split the church and poison the world with your heresies. On these grounds, in order to cleanse the world of such contagion and to destroy so rotten a member, with the full accord of the councilors and our fellow citizens, in the name of the

Father, the Son, and the Holy Ghost, hear now our final verdict: We sentence you, Michael Servetus, to be led in fetters to Champel, there to be bound to a stake and with your book to be burned alive, until your body has been changed to ashes; thus will your life be extinguished as a warning to others who do as you have done."

Servetus collapsed to his knees under this sentence, for its unexpected severity struck him like a thunderbolt. An animal in deadly peril, he cried, "Have mercy —the sword, the sword!" Calvin described this despairing cry of a perishing creature as "the bellowing of a Spanish cow."

Farel, acting both as executioner and as spiritual adviser, admonished Servetus that to obtain the mercy of the sword he would have to recognize and confess his error.

Servetus threw himself in deadly anxiety at Calvin's feet, begging his pardon if he had ever offended him. Calvin turned his back to him, saying, "I am not prosecuting any personal offense, but the outrage you have committed against God." Again Farel adjured him to acknowledge his crime. "I have not sinned! I die innocent!" cried the doomed man. At this the old man, irritated, threatened that if the prisoner persisted in posing as innocent he would let him alone and would refuse him spiritual comfort before the funeral pyre. Servetus was silent and the dreadful journey began.

In front a few horsemen and councilors, then Servetus with Farel, surrounded by soldiers, and the curious crowd, the supernumeraries and instigators of every public outrage. So across the Bourg-de-Four square, up the Rue de Saint-Antoine to the gate and out toward Champel. Calvin, the historian of his own deed, writes: "Although he was free to say whatever he wished to say, he was as dumb as a block of wood; no confession of any kind came from his lips."

The procession stops on the hill of Champel. All preparations have been made. The executioner is ready for his victim. The people seek good places. The multitude begins to pray. Farel demands of the heretic that he deepen the devotion of the people with his own praying. Servetus obeys. The monotonous prayer chant rises on the air like the humming of gigantic bees in the woods of Champel. In silence Servetus mounts the swaying, unstable heap of twigs and wood, in whose midst rises the stake to which the executioner binds him with iron chains. The lonely man is not alone. Near him hangs in iron chains a book with the proud and godly title, *Christianismi Restitutio* (*The Restoration of Christianity*) his work, his damnable crime, his undying deed.

On his head rests a crown of leaf-work besmeared

with sulfur. Before his eyes dances the light of the terrible torch. An awful cry of terror breaks from him, vibrates the stake on which his martyred body hangs, bores into the hearts of the onlookers, cleaves the air like a hunted bird, and resounds like a bell through all eternity: "Jesus, Son of the eternal God, have mercy on me!" The moist twigs will not burn. Out of the smoke and vapor rises ceaselessly the agonized cry to the eternal God. Merciful souls bring dry twigs to end the torture. The voice out of the burning thornbush grows weaker, smothered by the crackling of the flames. After an hour the living torch is extinguished.

Michael Servetus, forty-two years old, a refugee from Tudela in Spain, home of the auto-da-fe, hunted in France by the Inquisition, executed in Geneva by the minions of Calvin, an outlaw and hunted man, denied peace throughout his whole life, exterminated by his fellow men like a wild, mad animal!

Melanchthon, the mild and learned humanist, writes with his own hand: "The municipal council of the Genevan Republic, four years ago today, gave for all posterity a pious and memorable example of how unholy blasphemies should be punished, when it executed the Aragonian Servetus. To all who took part in that event I wish good luck. I am only surprised that there are still men who condemn such severity."

Who was Servetus?

A saint, a heretic, a great physician.

Servetus was born on September 29, 1511. His father, a highly respected notary, hailed from Villanueva. His mother was French; her family name was Revès, and he was glad to add it to his signature at the beginning of his literary career. At fourteen he read Latin, Greek, Hebrew, and had mastered scholastic theology. He attended the University of Saragossa.

Over Spain lay the smoke of the Inquisition's fires. Since the Fourth Lateran Council in 1228—for three hundred years—the reek of blood and burning had wasted the thriving land, until under the mad rule of Torquemada, a little later, the face of every Spaniard was stiff with horror and dread. There was no sleep in the narrow streets through which the death carts made their stealthy way with leather tires on the wheels and muffled hoofs on the horses, carrying their victims to the flaying places of the spiritual courts. Such were the scenes under whose impress Servetus grew up.

At seventeen Servetus became a student in the famous law university at Toulouse. There, in the enlightened republic of Languedoc, he experienced the disturbing shock of a new world. The boy who for years had delved into the teachings of medieval scholasticism, to whose substance and severity Spain was still fully subject, heard here for the first time the call of spiritual freedom and independence that came out of the North. Secretly, in the night, he read the *Loci Theologici* of Melanchthon, and doubt gripped the young man with magical power. The staggering youth was torn by an overwhelming experience that gave direction to his destiny and inexorable impetus toward his catastrophe. Servetus discovered the Bible.

The Pandects flew into a corner. For hours and days he sat with a few like-minded friends and read—as he never had in the cage of scholasticism—the words of the gospel. With horror and ecstasy the young man saw how sorely he had been belied and betrayed; saw also that there was no bridge and no common ground between the eternal truths of this powerful book, the actual life and sufferings of Christ, and the lifeless doctrines of scholasticism which lived and thrived only on the blood of the heretic. "Ingemisco, contremisco, perhorresco, proh dolor, res flebilis orbi, viscera penetrantur"—"I groan, I quiver, I quake; O pain, sorrow for the whole world, that convulses me through and through!"

With pleasure Servetus accepts the opportunity offered by the father confessor of Charles V, Jean de Quintana, to accompany him as his secretary in the retinue of the emperor. Servetus needs inward clarity, and this draws him mightily toward Germany, the land of Luther, the land of religious freedom.

In the imperial train he traveled to Italy, where in

1529 in Bologna the double crowning of Charles V
by Pope Clement VII took place. On June 20, at the
diet of Augsburg, he witnessed the agreement of the
great religious politicians and became acquainted with
Melanchthon and the Strasbourg reformer, Martin
Butzer. With burning zeal the nineteen-year-old Spaniard followed the articles of the Augsburg Confession
as read by Melanchthon, and the *Confutatio* of Dr.
Ecks. Luther did not come. But when Butzer, repulsed
by Melanchthon and Chancellor von Brück, went to
seek out Luther at Coburg, young Servetus went with
him.

The meeting with the forty-seven-year-old Luther
was a great experience for the young man. Wholly under the impress of this man's attractive personality, the
secretary of the Spanish father confessor defended the
Wittenberg heretic wherever he could. With painstaking zeal he read the *Theses Against Eck,* the *Babylonish
Captivity*, and the *Treatise Against Erasmus.* But, fully
as he admitted the spiritual necessity of a separation
from Rome and made Luther's arguments his own in
this respect, he perceived even then in Luther's doctrine
of a servile will the fearful danger which Calvin's
gloomy, paralyzing tenet of predestination—the im-
mutable fixing of all good and evil beforehand—conjured up as the final consequence of this doctrine of
a dead free-will.

For Servetus the Bible, this "heaven's book," was the deliverer from the depression and hopelessness of his young soul. To dig this book free from the rubbish of a thousand years became the work of his life; ever more clear and overpowering stood forth before him the form of the historical Jesus, and with irrepressible energy he fought for the primal purity and historical truth of this human career and its eternal idea.

Out of this soil grew also his opposition to the dogma of the Trinity. The trinitarian doctrine was one of the chief tenets of medieval scholasticism and it remained one of the main points of evangelical theology. The Christ of Servetus, however, was not the Christ of the theological schools but the Christ of the Bible and of conscience. The Bible knows nothing of the dogma of the Trinity. Not until the Council of Nicæa (325) did it become a fundamental tenet of Christian doctrine.

The tragedy of Servetus lay in the fact that at the moment in which he made known the needs of his knowledge and faith to the leaders of the German Reformation at Augsburg, evangelical dogma was attaining its final form in the Augustan Confession, and the victorious Reformation was changing Luther's idea of tolerance, held high by him from the beginning, into stern compulsion to orthodoxy.

Thus was sealed the sinister fate of Servetus, who wanted nothing but a pure and unhypothecated piety in the spirit of the Bible. His life became that of a breathless, hunted animal. By Catholics and Protestants alike he was pursued with undying hatred. At Basel he was banished, in Regensburg he was jeered, in Strasbourg they wished him to be drawn and quartered. Three times he was tried for his life. In Paris he was acquitted, in Vienne he was saved by flight after being condemned to death, in Geneva his deadly fate overtook him.

Opponents in his own time dimly suspected what, later, his spirited defender, Tollin, clearly recognized: Servetus was the pioneer of a new world of faith. The sixteenth century saw not only the birth of the Protestant Reformation, the work of Luther, Calvin, Melanchthon, Zwingli; it was with equal revolutionary power the century of the Catholic Reformation; through the decisive act of the Council of Trent (1545–1563) it shaped the modern Roman Church. Beside the Augsburg Confession of the year 1530, however, beside the decrees of the Council of Trent in 1563, there appeared in 1553 the chief work of Servetus, his radical advocacy of the restoration of Christianity, the right to freedom of conscience—as Tollin calls it, the church of Spinoza and Kant, of Lessing and Fichte, of Herder and Schleiermacher; the church without names, the church without people, for Servetus was no politician, no man with a program, nothing but a confessor.

His work was his life. He wished to see the oneness of God, in which he believed, become a reality in all earthly affairs springing from the same root. Religion and nature, science, ethics and theology were for him only different husks of one and the same truth. Thus he represented a religious humanism and possessed the universal world feeling of the Renaissance, but refined and guided by an elementary and undogmatic piety.

The world of faith in the heart of Servetus was cut off from the world round about him. The stake and torch smothered his voice. That voice would have been called upon to lead the ethics of western science out to the spirit of Christlikeness, to found securely the bridge between God and science, between theology and medicine, which in truth even today is not yet built.

Servetus achieved one stroke of scientific genius, the discovery of the minor circulation of the blood, that fundamental starting-point of modern physiology, and he hit upon it as a necessary element in his system of faith. A bold and fortunate stroke of scientific research thus took on an added significance: an exact interpretation of nature had been achieved through the spirit of religion. Almost always the great discoverers and wideners of the world picture have been heretics to the faith. The faith-world of Servetus, being free of dogma, stood wide open to the freedom of research. "If you believe that the Godhead dwells somewhere within, where else can it dwell than in man? Man is more completely filled with God than the world has ever yet perceived."

After Augsburg Servetus begins an uncertain life. He resigns his court position and betakes himself to Basel and to the famous preacher Oecolampadius. The latter, after a brief misunderstanding, shows him the door and calls him "a Jew, a Mohammedan, a blasphemer possessed of the devil."

The twenty-two-year-old Servetus, the roving knight of his idea, wends his way to Strasbourg in order to find Bucer and Captain Fühling. After a few days Bucer writes: "This godless man should be cut into little pieces and the bowels torn out of his body." In Basel the printing of his first book, *Concerning the Errors of the Trinity*, was forbidden, so he had to go to Hagenau, where it appeared in 1531.

Already the call to the funeral pyre is resounding loudly, but Servetus does not hesitate to publish in the following year his *Dialog on the Trinity,* a magnificent presentation of evangelical doctrine, but a still sharper and more challenging renunciation of trinitarianism.

The printing of these books has used up all the author's savings. His kin has repudiated him. Reviled and despised, cursed and hunted, he flees to France, where, in 1534, under the name of Michel de Villeneuve, he finds a position as proofreader for the book printers Melchior and Kaspar Drechsel in Lyons, who pity the half-starved student. Soon he surprises his employers with his profound knowledge of the ancient tongues, by means of which he obtains an order to prepare a new edition of Ptolemy's Alexandrian Geography.

This book, which appeared in 1535, was a complete success. It was the first recognized attempt at a comparative geography—long before Alexander von Humboldt. The brilliantly written and handsomely printed work found a splendid market and brought to Servetus the friendship of the physician Symphorion Champier, an enthusiastic Galenist and prolific writer, physician in ordinary to the Duke of Lorraine, whose books were being published by the Drechsels.

Champier turns the eyes of the young Servetus to the world of the healing art and smooths his way to Paris. In thankfulness for his fatherly help, Servetus writes a defense of him against the attacks of Professor Fuchs of Tübingen.

The year 1536 finds Servetus in Paris. In the colleges of the Ile de Cité and around Notre Dame seethes the spiritual cook-shop of the European world.

We know the bold strokes of his manuscript written

at that period, when, as with tooth and nail, he was defending himself against the destiny of flight and condemnation. Amid the scenes of daily life his wholly introspective, indifferent gaze turns with a sort of dreamy humility toward things of the past. Frail and yet unbending, he is exalted high above the grip of destiny and the necessities of life. Seldom has a great figure been so completely annihilated or remained thus wholly without an inheritance to pass on to the world. We know of no one whom he trusted, no one who was there to lighten his pain. To the inquisitor at Geneva, who shamelessly made use of the fact of his wifelessness as a proof of his unchastity, he had to confess: "I felt that I was impotent because in my fifth year I was mutilated on one side and ruptured on the other."

In 1537 the first medical work of Servetus appeared in Paris. It dealt with the use of sirups (*Syruporum Universa Ratio*) and had the largest success of all his books. In a short time it ran through five editions. In harmony with the ideas of the Paris school, it fought against Avicenna and the Arabian method of boiling juices, and came out strongly for a therapy like that of Galen.

The special feature of that year was the serious anatomical study of Servetus. He was the first theolog to touch the work of God with his own hands, to dissect with skilled fingers the bodily substance, seat of virtues and vices, and to seek to bring the confusion of the organs into harmony with the spirit of the holy Scriptures. Thus he became, with the anatomist Guenther von Andernach, the worthy successor of the great Vesalius.

About the time his book appeared, Servetus gave a well-attended lecture on astronomy and astrology, among his hearers being Pierre Paulmies, later archbishop of Vienne. In his vehement discourse he attacked the physicians of the faculty, calling them asses and ignoramuses, and soon afterward (March 18, 1538) he was standing, accused, before the high court. The faculty demanded the death of the foreigner who dared to insult the high priests of science and pretended to forecast from the stars the course of destiny. Servetus won a brilliant acquittal by means of his written defense, *Apologetica Disceptatio pro Astrologia,* in which he maintained that he was as good a Christian as the doctors who were prosecuting him.

About this time the fateful meeting with Calvin in Paris must have taken place, an acquaintance which, after sixteen years, was to be so horribly renewed in the dungeon at Geneva. "Remember sixteen years ago in Paris: did I not try then to win you for our Lord? If you had thrown in your lot with us at that time I would have taken pains to reconcile you with all good servants of God. But you raged against me and calumniated me. Now pray for mercy to God, whom you have blasphemed by trying to extinguish the three beings that constitute Him." The irrepressible life-and-death struggle between the two men had begun. The irregular, abnormal mask of Calvin, the small, thin, sapless face, hard as bone, unnaturally prolonged by the gigantic nose and the protruding chin-beard, hid within it the fearful hatred then conceived until the day of reckoning should come. Kretschmer has referred convincingly to the peculiar affinity of Savonarola, Calvin, and Robespierre: idealism, fanaticism, despotism were the sources of their rending power.

After passing an examination Servetus settled down as a physician in 1540 in the little town of Charlieu, near Roanne; but it was only a short halt in his unsteady course. Over him, like a curse, hung the hostility of the world. A jealous doctor attacked him by night on the way to a patient, a scandal followed, and Servetus preferred to leave the place.

Again he sits as a proofreader in Lyons, and here his comfortless destiny seems to turn. Pierre Paulmier, his former auditor, now archbishop of Vienne, takes him as his physician in ordinary. The heretic lives in the archepiscopal palace. The past seems swallowed up. Twelve happy years Servetus passes in Vienne.

But for him rest and security are only the power-

source of an unwearying pressure of work. He is not
the man to let himself rest because of his calling, because of social success, because of his professional researches, or because he is growing older. Before his eyes
the great plan of his work takes form—the Encyclopedia of God, of Christendom, of Science, of Eternal
life. In entire innocence the fanatic of independence
turns his weapons against the fanatic of tyrannical
power, the spiritual overlord of Geneva. Through the
medium of the bookseller Jehan Frellon begins the
tragic exchange of letters between Calvin and Servetus,
the conversation between murderer and victim, between an individualist and a political theorist, which,
from word to word, opens up the abyss between them
and lets the inevitable crime go on ripening like an
evil fruit. Servetus sends Calvin extensive portions of
his manuscript, sends a copy of Calvin's own masterpiece, *Institutes of the Christian Religion,* in which he
has marked certain errors and defects, inaccuracies and
wrong conclusions, and awaits a reasonable answer;
but Calvin, thrown into a mad rage, falls upon him
with bitterest abuse and scorn. In a wild screed of February 13, 1546, signed with one of his countless pen
names, Charles d'Espeville, he completes the final
break. And on the same day, seven years before the
burning of Servetus, he writes to Farel: "Servetus has
just written to me and sent me an enormous volume of

his daydreams. He begs me to let him visit me. But I cannot do it. For if he came, so long as I had any influence whatever in this city, I could not suffer him to leave here alive." Servetus wrote him: "Since you fear I am Satan, let us go our own ways and make an end of it. Send back my manuscripts and fare you well."

For six years Servetus hovered over his work until it finally appeared early in the year 1553. This publication in the midst of the proscriptions of the Catholic Inquisition was a frightful risk.

Of this book, one of the rarest in the world, there exist today only three copies that have escaped the flames: one in the National Library at Paris, one in the State Library at Vienna, and one in the University Library at Edinburgh. Upon it we find neither the name of the author nor the place of publication, nor yet the name of the publisher. The full title is: *The Restoration of Christianity*: That is, the Recall of the Whole Apostolic Church to its Own Beginnings, thereby Completely Restoring the Knowledge of God, of the Faith in Christ, of Our Justification, of the Rebirth of Baptism, as Well as of the Partaking of the Lord's Supper; whereby, Finally, the Kingdom of Heaven is Restored to us, the Captivity of the Godless Babel is Done Away, and the Antichrist with his Followers is Completely Annihilated. The printing was done in great secrecy in Vienne by Balthasar Arnollet, at a hidden place outside of his public printing office, and there were a thousand copies.

This work, which appeared under such secret and hidden circumstances, as if it were the cursed deed of a conspirator or counterfeiter, contains, besides much contemporary and incomprehensible demonology, besides the simple and reverent postulate of an independent and truthful system of religious doctrine, one of the greatest and most significant developments of that epoch: the discovery of the circulation of the blood through the lungs!

The burning desire of Servetus to prove the facts in the case of the divine world-order by the undeniable results of exact science is fulfilled beyond expectation! Leaping over the erroneous ideas of a thousand years, he is the first to solve the secret of the interchange of substance between the universe and man, the entrance of the spiritual pneuma into the perishable animal shell, the eternal connection between the everlasting spirit of the world and the circling power of the flowing blood in the narrow body.

On page 170 of the *Restoration*, in the middle of the fifth book, which treats of the Holy Ghost, begins a detailed sketch of the physiology of the circulation of the blood. Servetus, in his teachings in regard to the Holy Ghost, seeks to prove the accuracy of the Old

Testament idea that the blood is the soul breathed into the earth clod by God (Deut. 12:23; Gen. 2:7). How well this really expresses the view of modern science can only be indicated here.

Servetus goes on to say: "In order to grasp this, one must next understand the creation of the life spirit (spiritus vitalis). The life spirit has its source in the left ventricle of the heart, and here the lungs in particular assist in its creation through the fact that in them takes place the mixing of the incoming air with the blood as it comes from the right into the left ventricle. This course of the blood is not completed, however, as commonly supposed, through the middle wall of the heart; the blood is driven in an extremely complex manner (magno artificio) out of the right ventricle on the long way into the lungs. There it turns golden (arterial) and is poured from the veins of the lungs into the arteries of the lungs. At this stage it mixes with the inbreathed air and is cleansed by the exhaling of the carbon (carbonic acid gas). And so it is finally drawn in again by the left chamber of the heart, thoroughly cleansed by the breathing of the lungs."

This classic statement of the minor circulation of the blood, an unpretentious and wholly hidden by-product of the Servetian attempt to reform the faith, is a real miracle in its precision and its blazing of a brand-new trail in science. It strikes squarely in the face the ruling idea of Galen, according to which the blood in the right ventricle goes through the pores of the dividing wall of the heart directly into the left ventricle. (*De Usu Partium*, vi, 10).

By what stroke of genius the thirty-five-year-old Servetus, otherwise a faithful follower of Galen, arrived at this new physiological conception is very difficult to guess, for he says nothing on that point. But there stands the incontestable fact that he was the true discoverer of the circulation of the blood through the lungs, which had been dimly surmised before him in 1315 by Mondino de Luzzi, was plagiarized after him in 1559 by Realdo Colombo, was recognized by Andreas Vesalius in 1555 in the second edition of his book on anatomy, and was developed by William Harvey a generation or two later, in 1616, into full knowledge of the fact that the blood circulates through the whole body.

William Harvey, of Folkestone in Kent, also experienced the opposition of his time. Not until twelve years after his tremendous discovery did he venture, in 1628, to make it public in his *Anatomical Inquiry into the Movement of the Heart and Blood*. He was a pupil in the great anatomical school at Padua, which had not lost the spirit of Vesalius. His teacher was Fabricius ab Aquapendente, who in 1570 discovered that all the vein

valves open toward the heart. As a physician at St.
Bartholomew's Hospital in London Harvey still retained his passion for research, and in him were united
a thorough knowledge of anatomy with the instincts of
a physician and long clinical experience. He was one
of the first prophets of experiment. He held the beating heart of the animal in his hand, but what riveted
his attention was not, as with Vesalius, the secret of its
anatomical structure; it was the rhythm of the movement. When the muscle of the heart contracts and
hardens, it must drive the blood that is in it into the
great artery. How much blood at each beat? Harvey
measured two ounces. Seventy-two times two ounces
a minute—that means 8640 ounces an hour—three
times the normal weight of the whole body.

The ingenious question regarding the amount of
blood driven out led to the solution of the riddle of
its circulation. For where would such an enormous
amount of blood come from or go to? There remains
for the reasoning mind no other way out than to admit
that the blood must return from the arteries to the
heart. Inevitably, Harvey's attention turns to the veins.
His teacher, Fabricius, had proved that the vein valves
open toward the heart. What other purpose can this
arrangement have than to regulate the direction of the
blood stream? The simplest hand-grip or constriction
shows the centrifugal movement of the venous blood

back into the heart. No longer a doubt: the blood flows out of the left ventricle through the arteries into the body and its organs, thence through the chinks of the tissue into the veins; the veins flow into the right side of the heart; first into the auricle, then into the right ventricle. There begins the minor circulation of Servetus: out of the right ventricle the blood pours into the lungs and thence back into the left auricle in order to complete the circuit in the left ventricle.

A storm of indignation rose against this revolutionary idea. Paris, under the leadership of Jean Riolau, denounced Harvey's discovery as the vaporing of insanity.

But for Harvey, who has found his way through the labyrinth of the body, debate or recrimination in such matters is a disorderly waste of time, from which he draws back shuddering. "It is much better," he says, "to seek in silence at home to become wise for one's own sake than to stir up storms by the hasty announcement of things that have cost a great deal of labor and pains, thus robbing ourselves of future rest and peace."

As court physician of King James I and King Charles I he was dragged into the civil war between the king's party and the parliamentary party. Amid the tumult of a battle he pulled a book out of his pocket and went on reading it until a bullet knocked it out of his hand. The old man wanted to work in peace, so he betook himself back to London and the solitude of his study. At seventy-four he died, June 3, 1654.

For the unfortunate Servetus there was no such peace of soul. His discovery opened wide the door of the science of life and of mankind, but his name was forgotten. The world was unwilling to praise a heretic so long as intolerance was in power. Religious intolerance destroyed the unity of will and belief realized by Servetus. Yet with his execution the age of enlightenment became inevitable.

As soon as the first copies of his work reached the hands of his enemies the serpent coiled tightly about his neck. An infamous intrigue was hatching to destroy him forever.

The reformer, Calvin, through his friend, de Trye, caused Servetus to be denounced by the Catholic Inquisition. On February 16, 1553, the Huguenot de Trye wrote to his Catholic relative in Vienne, Antoine Arneys: "There is among you a heretic who deserves, wherever he is, to be burned. I refer to a Spaniard whose real name is Michael Servetus, but who calls himself Villanovanus, a doctor. He has been in Lyons several times, but now lives in Vienne, where the book of which I speak was printed by a certain Balthasar Arnollet. So that you may not think this is mere rumor, I am sending you the title page as proof."

The stroke succeeded. The Grand Inquisitor of France, Pierre Ory, pounced with zeal upon the treason with which the heretic Calvin charged the heretic Servetus. The houses of Servetus and the printer Arnollet were immediately searched, but no trace of the dangerous work was found. Servetus was vouched for by his friend Paulmier. The Inquisition calmed down.

Calvin, however, will not let his victim go. Again come letters out of Geneva to Lyons, and this time Calvin delivers to his deadly Catholic enemy the final proof against his deadly enemy Servetus. He hands over to the Inquisition pages of the *Restoration* which Servetus had annotated in his own hand and sent to Calvin, whom he had always admired. Along with these pages he hands over two dozen letters dealing with their discussion of the Trinity and the rejection of infant baptism. This seals the fate of Servetus.

On April 4 Servetus and Arnollet were thrown into prison. Conviction was unavoidable. The Inquisition, however, seemed to get no very great satisfaction out of the heretic forced upon it by the Protestants. On April 7 Servetus succeeded in escaping. "The prison door was so that it seemed they wished me to get out." On May 2 the secret printing presses were discovered in Arnollet's home. Now the trial proceeded in the absence of Servetus. He was condemned to be burned in effigy along with his books, and on June 17, 1553, on the Place de Charnève in Vienne, this sentence was carried out so far as it could be. Five bales of his books died the death by fire.

At this point the most improbable thing happens. Servetus, in urgent need of getting away from the torch and stake of the Inquisition, suddenly appears in Geneva after a few weeks of uncertain wandering. It is Sunday morning, August 13, when he takes up his quarters at the Rose Inn. At the same time the trumpets proclaim loudly to one and all that every dweller in Geneva, on pain of a heavy fine, must attend Calvin's compulsory church service. Servetus betakes himself to divine service. There, mingling with the multitude, stands the man whom Calvin, seven years before, had sworn not to let escape alive out of his hands. "His evil star must have brought him here. Perhaps he had nothing else in mind than to travel through this city, for no one knows as yet why he did come here. He became known, and I have thought it necessary to have him arrested."

It is understandable that men have tried in many different ways to account for the strange flight of Servetus out of the prison of the Inquisition into the prison of his mortal enemy Calvin. Had he political intrigues in mind? Did he wish to bring about a new revolt of the Libertinists against the religious dictator? He himself states that he was going through Geneva to Naples in order to practise medicine in the large colony of his fellow countrymen there. But Calvin was right. It was his star that led him to Geneva, his desire for death, his lonely revolt against life in this form, the passionate impulse to confess and explain, and a proud disdain of earthly power and human intrigue. His union with God seemed to him stronger than his break with the world. Treachery, suspicion, the outcry of rage, the anxiety over his influence, the flood of slander—he saw all these clearly enough, but they found no admission into his faith-world, in which the Protestant Calvin still held the honorable place of a man troubled over matters of godly faith. He saw only the religious ideology of Calvinism, an ideology, as it seemed to him, caught in error, yet on the whole a pure doctrine with a soul in it. Had he known Calvin, the harsh dictator, the man driven by lust of power, hated by the people, tortured by physical suffering; had he seen beforehand the fearful work of this man's relentless, stony-hearted madness—the city of Geneva paralyzed by gloom, affliction and anxiety—he would have known what threatened him.

After his return from exile Calvin had organized a regiment of terror and reprisal, whose crazy excesses and heartless logic often had the earmarks of cruel comedy.

In Calvin's kingdom of God the worst sin was

laughing. All decorations were forbidden; all silk clothing, velvet slippers, hairdressing were proscribed; curling the hair was prohibited—women had to wear it smooth and with a knot. Nobody was allowed to wear a gold ring except on the day of marriage. Gloves had to be as plain as possible. Tailors did not dare, under pain of severe punishment, to invent a new style without permission of the authorities. The number and sequence of foods permitted on the table were limited. At weddings or feasts no sweets could be eaten; no more than ten persons could be invited—among the humbler folk not more than three. Artizans were forbidden to eat turkey or roast game of any kind.

Sport, of course, was under the ban, and so were play-acting and singing. Costumes and national customs were severely condemned. First names had to be strictly of biblical origin, and the traditional names used in Genevan families were rooted out. Dancing ranked as a heinous sin. No third person was allowed to give a present to newly-weds. No citizen or resident of Geneva dared eat or drink in a hotel. After curfew no foreigner was allowed to leave his quarters. A horde of spies and watchers of "the good and faithful people" patrolled the city, domestic servants were compelled to spy on their masters, children must betray their parents.

The details of this grotesque system of mutual torment might be multiplied indefinitely. Numerous exceptions to it were always provided for the well-to-do citizens, among whom Calvin must have counted himself, since he accepted from the council a fur-trimmed garment which had cost 450 francs, an unconscionable sum for that time. The rights of the poor were struck down by almost every one of the grotesque requirements of the laws. In the twenty-seven years between the return of Calvin and his death, more than 300 of the 10,000 residents of Geneva died by the sword or at the stake, and over 4,000 were thrown into prison. There was no check on authority—and no compassion. On March 16, 1545, the executioner, Jean Graujat, called Jean the White, was compelled to hack off his own mother's fingers and then to burn her to death at Champel.

If this city was a prison, its prison was a hell. It was the fate of Servetus to taste of its tortures. In a surprisingly short time the charges against him were ready. He was accused of heresy on thirty-eight counts, and during the long cross-examination new items of guilt were collected. Servetus asked for a defender before the council, since he was not acquainted with the rules and customs of the country. On August 27, fourteen days after his imprisonment, his plea was denied. Meanwhile his sentence had long been pronounced in secret. The council had sent an ambassador to the Swiss church to get its opinion. Calvin expressed his fear in numerous letters to Bullinger, Melanchthon and others that the decision would be disappointing for Servetus.

Servetus is losing his health in prison. He besieges the city council with vain cries for help. He asks "whether Calvin is taking pleasure in letting him rot in prison, where vermin are devouring him alive." He writes on September 22: "I demand that my false accuser be punished, that he be imprisoned as I am until the issue between us shall be wiped out by his death or mine, or by some other punishment. I demand justice, justice, justice!"

But the flood of wrongs mounts still higher for Servetus. Calvin is not satisfied with the victim's physical death; he desires his complete demoralization by means of dirt and sewage. On October 10 Servetus groans to the council:

"For three weeks I have been demanding and begging a hearing in vain. I beseech you, for Jesus Christ's sake, do not deny me what you would not deny a Turk who sought justice at your hands. I have necessary and important things to say to you. In regard to your order that something be done to keep me clean, nothing has happened, and I am more pitiable than ever. The cold torments me frightfully, and from my colic and my rupture I suffer other tortures which I am ashamed to describe to you. For God's sake, noble lords, help me either for pity's sake or for duty's sake. Written in your prison in Geneva. Michel Servetus."

Eight days later the damning verdict of the Swiss church governments of Bern, Basel, Zurich and Schaffhausen reaches Geneva. On October 25, Calvin writes to his friend Bullinger: "It is not known what will happen to the man. I think, however, that tomorrow in the council the sentence will be pronounced and he will be executed."

We know what happened. The court assembled the next day to sentence Servetus. On October 27 the fearful decree was read to Calvin's prisoner and was carried out on the same day.

Calvin, the cool observer, gives us this description: "When the news of his death sentence was conveyed to him, he seemed at first to be lost in thought; then he began to groan so that he could be heard afar off; after that he began to scream like a crazy man. In short, he had no more restraint than one gone insane. Finally his shrieks rose to such a pitch that he constantly beat his breast, crying in Spanish, Misericordia, Misericordia!"

Thus, at the height of his torture, ere the sun had begun to darken before his eyes and the flames to devour his body and his book, Servetus realized with the last departing power of his soul the true nature of the man in whom he had once thought to find God. With his last agonized look the heretic Servetus saw the truth: This deformed world of man is not God's world!

He took that comfort across with him.

MACROCOSM AND MICROCOSM

*The New Heavens of Copernicus and Kepler—
The Insect World of Swammerdam*

IV

MACROCOSM AND MICROCOSM

*The New Heavens of Copernicus and Kepler—
The Insect World of Swammerdam*

WHEN Jan Jacob Swammerdam, the apothecary, was thirty years old, his wife Barantje presented him with a son. As soon as the son, Jan Swammerdam, could distinguish the things of this world, he sat in his father's curiosity cabinet and saw and touched the interesting things collected there—animals, plants, gems, fine porcelains from the East Indies. When his father brought curious visitors, who had come from distant places, into his treasure room, which 60,000 florins could not tempt him to sell, their gigantic, unreal faces frightened the pale little Jan out of his dream world, whose intimate, secret power he heartily loved.

His grandfather was Jacob Dittrichssohn, from the little village of ´Swammerdam between Leyden and Woerden. But the East and West Indies Companies required thousands of ships for the salt herring that

lay in heaps on the wharves, and in the vaults of the
Bank of Amsterdam all the gold in the world was
collecting. So he moved into the big city to carry on
his thriving lumber business.

When Jan was born, February 12, 1637, Germany
was a smoking, never-extinguished heap of ruins.
French and Swedish troops were mangling the land.
Over the wilderness hung, in the west, the swelling
sun of absolutism, offering relief from misery, hunger,
and witchcraft madness. In the east the star of Bran-
denburg was rising in the European sky—Friedrich
Wilhelm, the Great Elector. In England the long
struggle between Charles I and Cromwell was beginning. Holland, however, was tearing along in an ever-
swelling stream of prosperity.

When Jan Swammerdam was a boy, Louis XIV,
almost of the same age, sat on the throne of France,
protected by his mother Anne. Jan waded in all the
puddles and ditches of Geldern and Utrecht, he collected worms, eggs, nests, beetles, midges out of the
earth and the brambles. All day long he roved through
the misty wildness of lonely places, through a ghost-
shadowed world of his own, far from the crowd. Soon
there were gathered between the bare walls of his
room many little crawling creatures of the primeval
world which no one knew about.

In Münster the bells are pealing forth the end of

the Thirty Years' War. For Holland peace is the apotheosis of its battle for national independence and religious freedom, which began in 1565 with the uprising of Egmont and Hoorn against the Spanish tyranny. The three and a half millions of the United Provinces rule the seas of the world; their colors wave over the gold mines that once belonged to Spain and Portugal, over Java, Ceylon, Sumatra, Guinea, over the Cape of Good Hope, over the coasts of Malabar and Coromandel. Out of pepper, nutmegs and cinnamon millions are made; the tulip craze breaks out, and thrifty farmers become speculators. The interest rate sinks to two per cent and gold flees across the border. Gigantic dikes, vast gardens, magic cities come into being. In Leyden, Kraneker, Utrecht, and Groningen universities are founded. The Holland newspapers print what they please. Intimidated by no absolutist despot, they menace the tyrannies of the West in France and England. The poor, the ill, the orphans and the insane are supported by the liberal contributions of the rich.

In Amsterdam, on the public square, the Nieuwe Kerk again rises toward the sky, and thousands of piles are driven to bear the dressed stone of the new City Hall, which Professor Tulp is causing to be erected in this city whose mayors for generations have been anatomists. In the narrow alleys of the Jewish quarter lives a sixteen-year-old youth, Baruch Spinoza, and not far away, in Jodenbree Street, dwells the lonely Rembrandt with his son Titus and his housemaid Henrikje Stoffels. Oppressed by scandalmongers and creditors, soon driven out of his home, he seeks refuge in the magnificent vision of "The Good Samaritan," which he painted in 1648.

Herein lies the secret of the destiny-shaping power of the human race, that a child can suddenly kneel down and find in the dust of the earth elements that change the view of the world. The boyish fingers of Jan Swammerdam dissect a despised nothing, a dead insect, a senseless bit of vermin, and discover the building-stones of a majestic architecture, a lofty, remote dwellingplace of life in whose depths heaven is mirrored. His eyes, snatched away from the dimensional concepts of the commonplace, must now, blinded by the wonders of the microcosm, lead a double life that both rejoices and torments. The difficulties of this study of nature become the joy of his life and transport him farther and farther from the sphere of human affairs. His timorous heart, at the end of his life, will rue as if it were a crime his invasion of that hidden world. But his great work, *Biblia Naturae,* will infallibly endure long after his death, under the protection of the power which lets nothing of value perish.

The seventeenth century was the century of vision;

but the churches, earthly stewards of God, had not been able to translate the dethroning of the earth from the center of the universe into a boundless widening of religious emotion. The spiritual results of the religious wars were poverty of heart and restlessness of mind. Earthly furor, the monomania of human power, did not perceive that above the clash of arms and the smoke of burning cities a new, overpowering idea was making itself felt. An unsuspected, monstrous, cosmic face unveiled itself, in which the advocates of faith failed to perceive the features of God. Thus reason and religion began perniciously to betray each other, theology and philosophy parted company, science and faith became enemies. A helpless and gnawing skepticism came into existence, until the revolt of the eye, the calm and magic power of figures, gave back to mankind the lost ability to regard the improbable as possible and to accept the same kind of intellectual hypothesis for the religious miracle as for the exact experiment of science.

A striking example of this warfare between the childish magic of the outward appearance of things and the critical judgment of incorruptible observation is presented by the change from the geocentric to the heliocentric idea which that age experienced.

The rebellious doctrine of Copernicus destroyed forever the childish faith—based on normal and healthy sense impressions—that man stands still on the earth and that the stars in the sky revolve around him.

Aristotle based the primitive geocentric religious concept upon the science and philosophy of his day. He established the naïve feeling of human security, the straight road from the middle of the earth into the realm of divine light, the close and intimate inter-relations of small and great, of the distressed and the exalted.

Copernicus pulled mankind out of this dream. Goethe writes in his *Farbenlehre:* "Among all the discoveries and convictions of man nothing has produced a greater effect on the human spirit than the teachings of Copernicus. Scarcely was the world known to be round and separate when it had to give up the tremendous prerogative of being the center of the universe. Perhaps there has never been a greater demand made upon man. Think of what he saw go up in vapor and smoke through this new knowledge: a second paradise, a world of innocence, poetry and piety, the testimony of the senses, the conviction of a poetic-religious faith; no wonder that men were unwilling to let this go on, that they opposed such a doctrine in every way—a doctrine that empowered and challenged those who accepted it to exercise a hitherto unknown freedom of vision and unimagined sweep of thought."

The church could not quietly accept the losses in

material and ideal possessions which the Copernican system conjured up. The world view of Aristotle, his philosophic and scientific system, was fully recognized by the theology of the Christian Middle Ages; it harmonized with the spirit of Christian doctrine, and the forerunners of the heliocentric teaching, Aristarchus and Seleucus, were already forgotten and outlawed in antiquity. "The unshakable, changeless, visible lordship of the church could find no secure home in a moving planet that circled with others about a common center. The ax was striking at the root of all existing ideas of nature; the deepest foundation of all the knowledge of the ages was undermined." *

With enormous tenacity the church set its face against the heretical views of modern astronomy. Lectures were delivered on the new cosmic theory, but not until 1540 did Copernicus venture to publish—through Osiander in Nuremberg—his book *De Revolutionibus Orbium Coelestium.* And not until he lay on his deathbed, May 24, 1543, did he hold in his hand the first copy of this work, dedicated to Pope Paul III. Along with Galileo's works, this epoch-making treatise later passed—in March, 1616—to the Index of Prohibited Books, and was forbidden to be read or taught under pain of damnation. There it remained until a century

* Henrik Steffens, *Polemische Blätter zur Beförderung der spekulativen Physik. 1829–35.*

ago, 1835, when a new edition of the Index put an end to the ban on Copernicus.

Almost all the standard universities—Pisa, Louvain, Salamanca—turned with wild hatred against the godless doctrine, and even Luther and Melanchthon declined it.

In Italy Giordano Bruno of Nola was a spirited follower of Copernicus. In his works, *De la Causa, Principio e Uno, De Minimo e Maximo, Contemplationi circa lo Infinito, Universo e Mondi Immunerabili,* he made a magnificent effort to give the new system a metaphysical significance—"the infinity of space filled with self-lighting worlds, the animation of these worlds by a soul, the relations of the highest intelligence, God, to the universe." In continuous flight after 1560, he taught in Geneva, Lyons, Toulouse, Paris, Oxford, Wittenberg, the "German Athens," in Prague, only finally, after his return, to languish in the leaden cells of Venice and after two years in the Inquisition prison at Rome to perish at the stake, February 17, 1600. "You are more afraid of the sentence you are pronouncing against me than I am!" he cried to the judge who uttered the death sentence.

The occurrence of the solar eclipse of August 21, 1560, marked the decisive turn in the life of the fourteen-year-old Tycho Brahe of Knudstrop. Against the opposition of his family he took up the study of astronomy and finally came to terms with his uncle, Steno Belle, on whose country estate he was allowed to erect a small observatory. There he saw a great miracle when going home on the night of November 11, 1572: he saw a new star in the sky—the Nova Cassiopeia. He did not trust his eyes, but called people to him, asking them to shake him and make sure that he was not suffering from an illusion. The newly discovered star of Tycho Brahe, who himself wavered irresolutely throughout his life between Aristotle and Copernicus, disturbed the divine unchangeableness of Aristotle's heavens. Careful investigation showed that the new star did not belong to the region of change which Aristotle located between the earth and the moon, but that it must be in the region of the fixed stars, the highest, divine, ever-unchanging sphere of Aristotle. Thus the *Mathematical Calculations Concerning a New Star, Never Before Seen, which I First Saw in November 1572,* published in 1573, was a hammer blow that left the whole Aristotelian cosmology in ruins.

Abolishing the "spheres" of Aristotle and establishing the changeability of the heavens—these are the great achievements of Tycho Brahe. When the great reformer of practical astronomy in 1577 established the fact that the comet whose appearance held all Europe in awe was moving far beyond the earth's orbit, in the eternal and changeless realm of Aristotle, the church authorities took action also against Tycho Brahe. After his break with the Danish royal family, he finished his life as imperial court astronomer of Rudolph II in Prague, where, in Benatky Castle, he studied the movements of Mars. At the age of fifty-five he died on October 24, 1601. "I seem to have lived not in vain," were his last words. With this he handed the torch to his thirty-year-old assistant mathematician, Johannes Kepler of Weil, in Württemberg, to remain in his care and keeping.

The exact reckonings of Tycho Brahe made possible Kepler's brilliant formulating of the laws of planetary movements. In 1609 he stated that (1) The path of every planetary body is an ellipse, one focus of which is occupied by the sun. (2) Every planetary body describes like sectors around the sun in like times (*Astronomia Nova*). On May 15, 1618, he wrote his third and most important law: "The squares of the periods of revolution of planets around the sun are in the same ratio as the cubes of their mean distances." (*De Harmonice Mundi*). "Finally I have brought to light the fact, and found it true beyond my highest hopes, that the entire nature of harmony is present in the movements of the heavens."

The towering form of Kepler embodies as no other the brilliant, divided state of mind of this memorable turn of the century. Lawgiver of gravitation, sun of that magnificent triple star—Copernicus, Kepler, Newton—inventor of the astronomical telescope, who in his *Dioptrice* was the first to explain the optical-physical relations of lens, prism, meniscus; publisher of the *Rudolphine Tables* (Ulm, 1627), prophet of mathematical certainty, of hard, disillusioning figures, he evinced once more the boldness of imagination, the artistic power of conception, the passionate dependence on faith as the prerequisite of brilliant scientific achievement, the thing that makes research superior to handiwork. In his *De Harmonice Mundi* he describes the earth as a powerful monster whose breathing, in the periodic sleep and waking due to the sun, causes the ebb and flow of the tides. This mythological power of imagination, inseparably bound up with extraordinary power of rational thought—for ten years earlier (1601) he had already ascribed ebb and flow to the earth's attraction—will always remain the basic principle of the creative faculty.

At about the same time the martyr, Morus, who died on the scaffold, and the martyr Campanella, who suffered for twenty-seven years in prison, destroyed (1639) the unwholesome and arbitrary boundaries between Utopia and reality; and the change in the world concept, in the rigid laws governing the bewildering infinity of the heavens, furnished a powerful incentive for the social rebuilding of mankind.

Kepler had to struggle desperately all his life to make enough to live on. Neither the emperor nor Wallenstein, to whom he gave important aid at Sagan in astrological researches, understood him. His aged mother was mixed up in dangerous witchcraft trials. Deadly ill and worn out, he went to Regensburg in the autumn of 1630 to lay his claims before the Reichstag. Six days after his arrival, on November 15, 1630, he died at the age of fifty-nine.

At the time of Kepler's death the great work of his contemporary, Galileo Galilei, was drawing to a close. Galileo's *Dialog Concerning the Ptolemaic and Copernican World Systems* appeared in 1632, and in it the most active spirit of this revolutionary astronomical generation gave the signal for the most disturbing, relentless and decisive battle over the new conception of the universe.

For Galileo's work reached its climax in the sacrificial and liberating achievement of proclaiming and idealizing the new physics as a new way of viewing everything in the world. That made him seem the most dangerous enemy of the church. The doctrine of the duality of the world, of earthly and heavenly matter, was overthrown by Galileo's verdict that all matter is earthly and alike. Thereby a fundamental condition of the mechanistic view was fulfilled, the gate into the enclosure of an unassailable eternity was ajar, and the way to the bold conquests of modern natural science lay open. What the Atomists and Stoics had already dimly suspected, what had been completely lost in the Middle Ages, now awoke in the writings of Galileo with elementary power of conviction, later to widen out on Newton's exact foundation until, in modern times, through the revelations of spectroanalysis, through the discovery of helium in both the earth and the sun, it became a self-evident proposition.

In 1610 Galileo, with his telescope, had already discovered the three satellites of Jupiter, the mountains of the moon, and the sun spots. In 1611 he made known the fact that the planets get their light from the sun, that Venus and Mars revolve around the sun. At the age of twenty-five (1589) Galileo was professor of mathematics in Pisa. Before that he had, as we know, solved the secret of the pendulum by observing the movement of a lamp swinging in the cathedral, and had discovered the laws of falling bodies through experiments at the leaning tower of Pisa. In 1608 he discovered the laws governing bodies on an inclined plane, in 1609 the law of inertia.

The arm of the Inquisition reached Galileo for the first time in Padua. On February 26, 1616, after the Inquisition had denounced his astronomical teachings as foolish, absurd and heretical, Galileo had to give his adversary, Bellarmin, in solemn conclave, the assurance that he would abandon entirely the idea of the dual motion of the earth around the sun and around its own axis, and never defend it in any way by spoken or written word.

Sixteen years Galileo lived alone, working in silence at Florence; then, however, knowledge drove the old man to make known the truth, and he felt the annihilating hand of the Inquisition. Dragged from prison to prison, tormented by the rack and by threats, he was compelled on June 22, 1633, in obedience to the hard terms of the Holy Office, to take this staggering oath:

"I, Galileo Galilei, sixty-eight years old, kneeling and with the holy Bible before my eyes and with my hands touching it, of heresy strongly suspected, swear that with honest heart and in good faith I curse and execrate all errors as to the movement of the earth around the sun and all heresies and every idea that is opposed to the holy church; I also swear in the future never to assert or say anything, either by speech or by writing, that could lay me under such suspicion; and should I know a heretic or one open to suspicion of heresy, I will make him known to the Holy Office or to the Inquisitor."

Galileo, now blind, sits for almost ten more years as a prisoner and outcast in his place of exile, Arcetri.

Not another line does he dare to publish, but he works on unceasingly. He dies on January 8, 1642. Only a hundred years later do his remains find the desired rest in the Santa Croce Church in Florence. Only his gilded forefinger, warningly raised and carefully protected, points at the lonely visitor in the Museum of Natural History in that city as a relic sacred to the freedom of science.

For it is the lasting glory of Galileo that he was the first to raise his voice for the freedom and worth of earth, that he defended reverence for living change against the idol of a stark and changeless perfection. No longer is the earth a place of eternal suffering. Passionately he protested that the earth was regarded as a sewer for the waste of the universe, that mere change awakened hatred. Change is not a sign of imperfection.

"Only with the greatest astonishment, yes, with the greatest inward repugnance, can I hear the attributes of unalterability, changelessness, freedom from all influence, ascribed to the natural bodies that make up the universe, as if these qualities were something superior and perfect, and, on the other hand, as if movability, changeability, producibility must signify something very imperfect. For my part, I regard the earth as worthy of highest marveling and interest precisely on account of the many diversified changes, alterations, new creations, and so on, that ceaselessly take place upon it. . . . Does it never occur to the people who believe this, that were earth as rare as the most treasured jewels and metals, there would be no princes who would not gladly give a great mass of diamonds and rubies and gold merely to buy as much earth as one needs in order to plant a jasmine bush in a little pot, or a Chinese orange, so as to watch it bud, grow, bring forth its beautiful foliage, its fragrant blooms and its lovely fruits?"

This confession of love for living things marks the true birth-hour of modern natural science.

A year after Galileo's death, Isaac Newton came into the world at Woolsthorpe (January 5, 1643), on the little farm of his father, who died before his birth. At the age of thirty, as a Bachelor of Arts at Cambridge, Newton had already begun his research in problems of gravitation; but not until 1682, after he had been working on it for sixteen years, did he publish his book, *Philosophiae Naturalis Principia Mathematica,* containing the world-law of gravitation, which after a long interval brought our idea of the universe to its present magnificent status. "The quantity of matter in each celestial body gives the measure of its attractive power, which is effective in inverse proportion to the square of the distance and determines the extent of the effect which not only the planets but all the stars in the heavens exercise on each other." (Alexander von Humboldt, *Kosmos.*)

Newton lived wretchedly, overwhelmed with honors in old age, but plagued with gout, rheumatism and stone trouble. He died at the age of eighty-four, March 20, 1727. When asked how he had discovered the law of gravitation, he answered, according to Voltaire, "By thinking about it ceaselessly."

The dispute over the forming of the modern view of the universe lasted 175 years. Almost two centuries this truth required, from its first dawning in the brain of Copernicus (1507), to reach acknowledged certainty through the proofs set forth by Newton (1682). Men die, are executed, tortured, must forswear and denounce, but the Idea is immortal. Acknowledgment of the truth, this noble human persistence—these cannot be destroyed by a thousand deaths. While war and business, the decrees of power, fill the historic hours with alarms, "ceaseless thinking" alters in wondrous wise the destiny of the world. When this suffering, this call comes suddenly to a man who steps quietly out of the ranks, he is immune to earthly judgments, and, whatever attitude the world may take toward him, be he Paul, Job or Jeremiah, his work is carried through and his truth becomes effective.

Over the humming insects of young Swammerdam beamed the unriddled heavens. He dared to see with

Newton's eyes, dared to pave his way with the thoughts of the brethren of his time, the thoughts of Bacon, Descartes and Spinoza. For the new philosophical movement had soon overcome the skepticism that followed the collapse of the scholastic-theological philosophy. Campanella, Ramus, a victim of St. Bartholomew's night, the Portuguese Sanchez, the Lübecker Joachim Jung fought for freedom from dialectics and the system of Aristotle. The fatal turning away from the transcendental was accomplished through the fault of the church. God and the soul could no longer be subjects for philosophy. Mathematics and physics fixed the boundaries of its thought.

Francis Bacon, English high chancellor and philosopher, revolutionized scientific research with his book, *De Dignitate et Augmentis Scientiarum* (1605). The most efficient method of perception is through experiments controlled by the understanding. The assertion of his great predecessor Paracelsus in *Experimenta ac Ratio* is made good: medicine is applied natural science. The beginning of knowledge is doubt. Reason passes judgment upon the experiment, the experiment passes judgment upon the object. The observation of facts with a theological purpose in view was strictly banned from Bacon's philosophical system. But Bacon the statesman was overthrown in 1621, condemned to imprisonment and dishonor, and his property confiscated.

Descartes and Hobbes had a still more immediate influence on natural science because of their manifold personal contacts. In their teachings the demand for a mechanistic-mathematical system of observing nature was finally fulfilled, thereby determining not only the course of science in their own time but also the mathematical-experimental physics of coming generations. The adoption of exact methods in medical science found its original impulse in the works of these great thinkers of the seventeenth century.

René Descartes of La Haye in Touraine, that passionate advocate of unimpassioned thought, who passed the winter of 1619 in Neustadt amid severe psychical and religious conflict at the beginning of the Thirty Years' War, found in the isolation of that little town on the Danube, at the age of twenty-three, the keynote of his philosophy, the application of the laws of geometry to natural science. "On November 10, 1619, filled with enthusiasm, I discovered the foundations of a marvelous science." Seldom is the birthday of a great idea so definitely fixed. In constant change of his dwelling-place he passed the decisive years of his work in the Netherlands before, in 1650, he died at the court of Queen Christina in Stockholm. Thus it is explainable that the spiritual schooling of Swammerdam was completed under the mighty impulse of the new rationalism.

Over Swammerdam's life lies a heavy shadow—the

dark and devouring hatred between father and son. The apothecary, a vain dilettante collector, could foresee no use which the innumerable insects and snails in his son's room might serve. Collections of objects of nature in that speculative period were a favorite subject of capital outlay, which satisfied the intellectual hunger of the rich. Large sums were spent for the acquisition of these curiosities. In 1717 Peter the Great paid the anatomist Ruysch 30,000 florins for his collection, injected and prepared under his "lynx eyes and fairy hands." For the elder Swammerdam, however, the son was a make-believe collector. He wished him to be a clergyman, and only after a great struggle was Jan allowed to begin his anatomical studies at Leyden at the age of twenty-four. Then he studied for two years under the eminent teachers, Jan van Horne and Franciscus de la Boe-Sylvius, along with his friends Regnier de Graaf, who later discovered the follicle of the ovary, and Nicolaus Steno, the Dane.

As a medical student Swammerdam undertook a journey to Paris in 1664. On the way, as he related in a letter to his friend Steno written on June 28, 1664, he discovered the valves in the human lymphatic system while staying in the home of Tanaquil Faber at Saumur.

In Paris he began his deep, lifelong friendship with Melchisedec Thévenot, former French ambassador to Genoa, a man of the world and courtier of Louis XIV.

The chevalier took a fancy to the queer young fellow
and entertained him with his friend at the country
estate of Issy. There he was a silent, scarcely noticed
guest at the brilliant fêtes of Paris society. Only occasionally did he trouble himself to show the astonished
ladies and gentlemen the objects of his activities as a
collector; "then, however, he put to shame the idle
gossip of the dilettanti with his wordless art," writes
Boerhaave, the tardy rescuer of his work.

Through the Dutch ambassador at the French court,
Conrad von Benningen, Swammerdam obtained permission to dissect bodies at the hospitals of Amsterdam.
Back he went to Holland, and in the "Society of
Learned Physicians" made a name for himself in his
native city by means of important demonstrations of
the spinal marrow and the membranes enclosing the
brain. On February 22, 1666, he became a doctor of
medicine through a highly regarded and much attacked
work on breathing. On the title page of the book, which
is dedicated to Thévenot, appear two snails, united. In
1668 Swammerdam fell ill of malaria, and after that
he was never free from suffering. His father's demand
that he do something practical and earn some money
grew ever more insistent. The Grand Duke of Tuscany
visited him in 1668 in company with Thévenot. Swammerdam took a butterfly that was still wrapped in its
chrysalis, stripped off the shell, drew out the butterfly,

spread out all its parts, the feet, the wings, the proboscis, and showed them to the duke, whose enthusiasm was so great that he offered him 12,000 florins if he would come to Florence. In 1669 Swammerdam's *Historia Insectorum Generalis* was published in Utrecht.

This work founded the science of biology. Two Italians in Rome, Francesco Redi and the talented Malpighi, who simultaneously (1665) discovered the red blood corpuscles, had first directed the attention of science to insects; but Swammerdam was the first to describe their makeup and to apply that wonderful instrument, the microscope, to their study and thus to make possible a basis for their systematic classification. "Large and small creatures have equal value for research; indeed, the small ones, because simpler, are the more important for the scientist." Swammerdam was able to put an end to the erroneous belief in the self-generation of small insects out of slime, and thereby confirmed one of the great postulates of Harvey, who in 1651 offered proof that all creatures come from pre-existing eggs. "Omne vivum ex ovo! I leave it to any intelligent man to judge whether a creature in which so much art, order, wisdom, and the almighty arm of God is perceptible was generated out of putrefaction or by chance. Must not the future say No? I regard that as certain."

Almost at one stroke several discoveries now loom

up. To whom belongs the honor of discovering the microscope is a moot question. Galileo speaks in 1614 of his instrument, which makes fleas look as large as sheep. Antony van Leeuwenhoek, however, must be regarded as the founder of microscopic anatomy. This curious, self-taught man, who in near-by Delft was continually inventing instruments of hitherto unknown power, succeeded by their use in achieving the memorable discovery of the tiny creatures known as infusoria (November 8, 1675). He never sold an instrument or taught anybody how his were made. For ten long years (1702–1712) he refrained from publishing anything because he had been accused of an inaccuracy. When he died in 1745 at the age of eighty-eight he had succeeded in magnifying objects 270-fold and left behind him 419 microscopes, which are now in the British Museum.

Swammerdam's preformation theory—that generation is only the unfolding of parts already present—that the butterfly is already complete in the larva—has a right to be regarded as the beginning of the modern evolutionary theory. It had the most decisive influence upon the great minds of his time—Spallanzani, Leibniz, Haller. Kaspar Friedrich Wolff, through his studies of the embryo, was the first to turn the doctrine of the origin of species into the right paths (1759).

Obsessed by his work, Swammerdam bought and collected insects from all parts of the world. His social relations became ever more perplexing. When his fatherly friend Thévenot induced him to go and settle in Paris, he and his father came to the final parting of their ways. The apothecary forced the son to come back to Amsterdam. He refused to send him any money and withheld his clothes. In order to soften the old man's anger, the son spent useless months setting his father's collection in order. His health became ever more fragile. Only with the greatest effort could he develop his method, begun in 1667, of filling the blood vessels of anatomical preparations with colored wax. In 1672 he presented his discovery to the Royal Society of Scientists in England with a model of the human womb. In order to obtain funds for him, Thévenot tried to sell his collections, but, as usual in cases of need, there was no purchaser. A treatise on bees, which he completed the following year, he handed over to some stranger without troubling himself to see what became of it.

Swammerdam's unremitting work became more and more like a disease that was devouring body and soul. All day long he continued his observations, and then wrote throughout the night. From six in the morning till midday he sat in the glaring sunlight in order to see without shadows and without magnifying instruments. The rest of the time he worked with a microscope which Samuel van Musschenbroek had made over. In comparison with Leeuwenhoek's apparatus it showed essential improvements: six different, interchangeable lenses, a tripod that left the hands free, a diaphragm mechanism. To this instrument belonged needles and a knife so fine that they had to be sharpened under a magnifying glass. After fixing and hardening, the insects were prepared under water, as zoologists still do it today.

"From the beginning of nature study to our own time," writes Boerhaave, "nobody has been able to equal his work." But the greater his art became, the deeper his gaze penetrated into the secrets of the microcosm, the wilder became his unrest. "With a thousand anxieties, gnawings of conscience, and up-welling reproaches of his God-fearing heart, with sighs, sobs and tears" he completed his work. His disgust for the world and for himself mounted higher and higher. Only greed of fame, he thought self-accusingly, had driven him to undertake such great and heavy labors; he has misused the glory of God as a pretense. His own religious objections to his dissecting activities become ever more numerous. In his agonizings of conscience he asks his friend Jan Tielens to introduce him to An-tionette Bourignon. On April 29, 1673, he writes to her, on August 17 he receives an answer, and from that time forth this strange woman never lets go of him.

Antoinette Bourignon, easily the most curious phe-nomenon among the feminine religious ecstatics of the seventeenth century, not excepting Anna Garcia, Armelle Nicolas, Jeanne Marie Guyon, and Anna Vetter, was born in 1616 in the Flemish city of Lille. When still a child she ran away from home in the garb of a friar. In 1650 she conducted a home for children in Lille, mistreated and tortured the children, whom she believed to be possessed of the devil, and fled to Ghent and Mechelen, where the parson Johann de Cort fell completely under her power. De Cort, with whom she contracted an "evangelical marriage," was the possessor of the island of Nordstrand. This island off the coast of Holstein he had handed over to Jansenist refugees from France, and there the Bourignon decided to set up a "refuge of the godly." Next she lived with three men in an isolated house on the shore in Amsterdam. Here Swammerdam first fell in with her, and as a sick friend, a "Cartesian," begged her to help him.

De Cort was imprisoned for debt, and later journeyed alone to Nordstrand, where he is said to have been poisoned. This left the Bourignon sole heir to the island. For eleven months she hid herself, very ill, in the home of a merchant in Haarlem. On June 13, 1671, she landed with five followers in Tönning and lived for a year under the protection of the duke in Gottorf. She was constantly gaining new recruits. From Hamburg, from Friesland she attracted whole families. She bought a large house in Husum, on the mainland near her island,

and there set up a printing press from Holland in order to scatter abroad her writings in the French, Dutch and German languages.

The reformed clergy turned against her. The affair developed into a fearful scandal. The Bourignon and her disciples fled from place to place. In 1674 the printing press was seized by the authorities and the duke wished to have her imprisoned for life in Tönning; but Major General van der Wyck, who was to execute the order, became her enthusiastic convert and reconciled her with the duke. Before the Danish War she fled to Hamburg, and there the priests protested in 1677 against allowing her to remain in that city. She found refuge on the estate of Baron von Lützburg in East Friesland, where she became the superintendent of a hotel and poorhouse. But even here she accused the inmates of magic and, hidden under bedding, fled to Franecke in West Friesland, where she died, October 16, 1680, at the age of sixty-four.

Swammerdam's last work—on ephemera—appeared in 1675, though he had begun it eleven years before. This enormous biological treatise is full of pietistic thoughts. The last sentence is: "It grows, it is born into the world, it is a worm, it sheds its skin twice, it becomes adult, it generates, it lays eggs, it grows old and dies at last—all in the brief period of five hours."

The significance of this summary of a lifetime is rather staggering.

In the autumn of that year Swammerdam undertook a journey to Schleswig to see Antoinette Bourignon. In the following year he went as her ambassador to Copenhagen to seek an end to her persecution, but he found closed doors. At this point the father is most deeply stirred and embittered. He breaks up housekeeping in 1676 and cuts off the son with a yearly allowance of twenty florins. At the age of forty Swammerdam finds himself in the street, beggared and roofless. The few friends that he has abandon him. Thévenot alone sticks to him.

The next year the father dies. The fearful, lifelong torture comes to an end. The son inherits barely enough to live on without fear of starving. Strife with his sister over the property, however, robs him finally of physical and psychical security. He never leaves his room again. His malaria grows steadily worse. In 1680 his property is sold at auction. Confusion and ruin fall upon him with irresistible force. He dies on February 15, 1680, at the age of forty-three. "Indefessus Scrutator Naturae" —"Tireless Searcher of Nature"—is the inscription on his last narrow house at Amsterdam.

Because of his early death Swammerdam's most important work was left unfinished. Yet the buffetings of fate were even then not at an end. He had handed over his manuscript to his true friend Thévenot. The translator, Wingendorp, in Leyden, refused to allow it to be published. The matter was taken to the courts. But even Thévenot did not have the means to publish the work. At his death it came into the hands of the painter Soubert. From him the Parisian anatomist Duverney bought it for fifty dollars, and finally, in 1727, the royal physician, Boerhaave, a true protector of the treasures of classical medicine, succeeded in obtaining the work for 1500 florins. Ten years later, on Swammerdam's one hundredth birthday, there appeared, under Boerhaave's direction, a handsome two-volume folio edition of his *Biblia Naturae,* his greatest contribution to science.

Swammerdam was a leader and a victim of that colorful and gloomy, that barbaric and highly civilized century, which had fallen into the intoxication of the infinitely great and the infinitely small, the sober passion of numbers and the thrill of an actuality that was magnificent beyond all imagination. Rembrandt, whose genius put the touch of the divine into the human face, and Callot, who crowded human deeds into the abysmal smallness of insect life, are the artistic poles of this age, Cyrano de Bergerac and Swift the literary shapers of the imaginary world of giants and pigmies.

The fate of Swammerdam and his century has found its final expression and its definitive explanation in the sentences of his contemporary and brother in suffering, Blaise Pascal (1658):

"What is man when viewed as a part of infinity? Who can comprehend it? But in order that he may see another, equally astonishing marvel, let him delve into the smallest thing that he knows. A midge, for instance, presents to him, in its tiny body, parts that are incomparably smaller—legs with bands, veins in these legs, blood in these veins, moisture in this blood, drops in this moisture, vapor in these drops; let him exhaust, while he divides these last things still further, all his powers of imagination, and let the last subdivision to which he can attain be now the subject of our consideration. He may think, perhaps, that this is the final, smallest thing in nature. In it I will show him a new abyss. . . .

"Let him descry therein an infinity of worlds, each of which has its firmament, its planets, its earth in the same relations as our visible world; on that earth animals, finally also midges, in which he again sees what he saw in the first, and yet again in these he finds the same things again, without end or rest. Let him lose himself in these wonders, which have power to make their smallness as amazing as the others their greatness. For who will not be moved to wonder when he sees that our body, imperceptible as it seems in the immeasurable universe, at the same time is a colossus, a world, yes, a universe, in the presence of that uttermost smallness to which human thought cannot attain.

"He who thus regards himself will doubtless be startled to see himself suspended, as it were, between the two abysses of infinity and nothingness, from both of which he is equally far removed. He will tremble in the perception of this miracle; and I believe his curiosity will change to amazement and he will be more inclined to contemplate it in silence than to delve into it with presumption."*

* Pascal, *Thoughts*, Vol. I, Article 4.

KASPAR FRIEDRICH WOLFF

Founder of the Evolutionary History of Mankind

V

KASPAR FRIEDRICH WOLFF

Founder of the Evolutionary History of Mankind

THE secret of how man became man was revealed in certain decisive points by a definite creative act of Kaspar Friedrich Wolff of Berlin. His life is the drama of an almost blameworthy modesty. During his career he encountered partly bitter and partly good-natured opposition to his ideas. He left his fatherland, which would not vouchsafe the smallest opportunity for his work. For twenty-seven years he labored apart from European science, poor and contented, in the shadow of the St. Petersburg Academy.

Forty-five years after the publication of Wolff's discovery, eighteen years after his death, his wholly neglected and forgotten work of genius was rescued from the rubbish heap of dusty erudition by a German translation. The names of his erring opponents have a secure place in the world of culture; but historical piety, otherwise so meticulous, has not yet pardoned this talented man for the anonymity of his private life.

135

No picture, no tablet recalls him to the memory of his native city, which has never been sparing of monuments. Berlin, where so much greatness and intellectual brilliancy has come to fruition—but only occasionally reached the outside world—has forgotten this Berliner. The two hundredth anniversary of his birth, in 1933, brought no oratory in his honor.

Perhaps the unpardonable neglect and silence of posterity is explained in part by the fact that he left no record of the day of his birth. For it is rare indeed to find a man who renounces this symbolic and documentary proof of earthly existence.

Goethe was one of the first to become aware—through his studies on the comparative morphology of plants—that he had a significant and unknown predecessor in Kaspar Friedrich Wolff. In 1817, in a supplement to his *Metamorphoses of Plants* entitled "Discovery of a Worthy Predecessor," he described Wolff's work and appearance so far as he could do so from the scanty information given by the physician Mursina. The quatrain which he attached to these facts has been only very scantily fulfilled in the few later writings which Kirchhoff, Waldeyer and Haeckel have dedicated to Wolff's scientific significance:

> May this show the world your ways;
> Noble scholars soon will praise
> Thoughts that you have touched to flame
> When the many learn your name.

Wolff's life fell into the active and brilliant period of Frederick the Great. His work is a magnificent example of the elementary awakening of creative power in Germany. While in France the corrupt system of Louis XV was driving the people and country inevitably into the redeeming but barbaric catastrophe of the Revolution, there was drawing to completion a wonderful drama of progress—the reentrance of Germany into European civilization. The devastation of the Thirty Years' War is past. The cultural guardianship of France is being shaken off. The thought-world of the new dawn and its great trail-blazers, Voltaire, Rousseau, Diderot, is going through a specific change in German atmosphere and German emotions. The heroic epoch of German classicism is beginning: The Prussian idealism of Kant; Winckelmann's transformation of the cultural arts; Lessing, Klopstock, Wieland, Herder, Goethe and Schiller are shaping world-stirring works of classic German literature; Bach, Händel and Gluck are creating German music that will never die.

It was no accident that German science was the last cultural element to be restored, and that at first its creative powers still wandered homeless over German lands. For nowhere is it more difficult to reestablish a violently interrupted intellectual continuity than in the realm of research. Science requires for its work a complicated and well organized apparatus; it needs time and an undisturbed concentration upon the work in hand. In part the apparatus was not yet created, in part it was completely destroyed, in part it was in the possession of a tyrannical bureaucracy which, long cut off from the stream of creative research, was unable to tolerate a new spirit in its midst. Not until the questionable scientific movement of romantic nature-philosophy arrived at the beginning of the nineteenth century was there any one to support the new ideas; and that movement had the difficult task of completing the revolutionizing of the German high schools and the winning over of German savants to the intellectual awakening.

Now it becomes understandable why such a self-reliant and independent phenomenon as Kaspar Friedrich Wolff had to stand alone. In the Berlin of Friedrich Wilhelm I he came into the world in 1733. His father was a master tailor. That is all we know. At the age of twenty he began his studies in the Medico-Surgical College.

Berlin had just begun—extremely late—to lead a scientific life of its own. In the time of the Great Elector there was only one woman, Justine Siegemundin, née Dittrichin, the wife of a Schleswig captain of horse, who completed an original medical treatise.*

* *Chur-Brandenburgischen Hoff-Wehe-Mutter,* published at Cölln a. d. Spree in 1690.

With the accession of the Hohenzollern dynasty to the supreme power Berlin's intellectual birth begins. In 1701 Elector Frederick III became King Frederick I at Königsberg, and on July 11, 1700, through the initiative of his wife Sophie Charlotte, who was a friend of Leibniz, the "Society of the Sciences" was founded. Its first president was Leibniz, and after it had made a long pretense of existence, Frederick the Great in 1744 allowed the "Academy of Sciences" to be created out of it—after its reorganization by the mathematician Maupertuis. Under the protection of the Academy the Anatomical Theater came into being in 1713, and eleven years later developed into the Medico-Surgical College. In 1710, on the occasion of the great pest epidemic, the Charité, the oldest Berlin hospital, was built. The first medical regulations in Berlin were entirely for military purposes. Never would the soldier king have given his consent for an establishment so very costly if his physician in ordinary, Holtzendorff, had not understood how to make clear to him the vital interest of the army in good surgeons. So also in Prussia medicine waxed great through the army.

The activities of the Medico-Surgical College, wholly designed as they were for the practical, led to this result: that in the Institute, whose instruction Wolff received, there were a number of competent handicraftsmen in the anatomical and surgical departments, but—with a few exceptions, including the then lately dead Georg Ernst Stahl, founder of animism and of the false phlogiston doctrine—no outstanding scientific teachers.

Wolff finished his studies at Halle. There, in 1759, at the age of twenty-six, he took his doctor's degree with his thesis, *Theoria Generationis*. This firstling of his works—perhaps unique in the history of medicine —marks one of the most important events in biological science. It lays the foundation for the modern evolutionary history of man, it discovers the first data for the cell theory, it shapes the fundamental facts for the doctrine of the evolution of plants. The *Theory of Generation* stood in complete opposition to all that the recognized scientific leaders of the century, Leibniz and Haller, were thinking and writing in regard to the origin and development of man. They were wrong. Wolff was right. Since Aristotle's *Concerning the Generation and Evolution of Animals* no work of like significance had been produced. Fifty years later Lamarck followed in his *Zoological Philosophy* with the first attempt at the history of descent (1809), and exactly a century after Wolff came Darwin's great work on *The Origin of Species*. Without the *Theory of Generation* this evolutionary sequence in the history of ontogeny and philogeny would not have been conceivable.

The story of evolution begins with Aristotle, who was one of the greatest zoologists of all time. It is astonishing what he already knew about the propagation of the lower forms of life, such as the cuttlefish. He knew of the virgin egg-laying (parthenogenesis) of the female bee, which, a thousand years later, was again discovered by Siebold. He knew that the shark produces a placenta, a fact that was long regarded as a myth or a figment of the imagination, until in 1839 Johannes Müller vindicated Aristotle.

The conflict over the embryonic development of the living creature, in which Wolff took so decisive a part, was already settled by Aristotle, imperfectly, indeed, yet completely in the sense of the theory of generation which he propounded: First the heart is formed as the beginning and center of the body. The internal organs develop earlier than the external, the upper before the lower. Very early the brain is formed, and out of it grow the eyes. The eternity of the individual is denied. Only the species or the race, which proceeds from like individuals, can be eternal. The individual itself, he says, is transient; it arises anew through the generative cell and returns through death to earth.

Two thousand years the wisdom of Aristotle lingered in the twilight, unused, degraded, distorted, theologically misinterpreted, until in the year 1600, in Padua, which seems to have an absolutely mystical flair for anatomical science, the disciple of Falloppio, Fabricius ab Aquapendente, the influential founder of the anatomical theater in that city, ventured upon the first primitive description of a human fruit in his book, *De Formato Foetu.*

For Aristotle the secret of generation was still hidden. In his doctrine the individual is developed by the union of certain germs of the male and female organisms. Harvey was the first to show in his *Exercitationes de Generationibus Animalium* (1651) that all created things develop from preexisting eggs. Harvey's case is one of the many striking examples of the intellectual blindness of gifted scientists. This great man, who was so near the truth, supported with his momentous authority the theory of the generation of the lower forms of life from mire.

Pure truth is seldom tolerated by contemporaries. Authority is mostly a strange mixture of the true and the false. In the same book that sets forth the fundamental fact that "every living thing comes from an egg" we find: "Certain creatures are made from materials already prepared, and are changed from one form into another. All the parts are born and shaped simultaneously through a single transformation. Insects are generated in this way."

Swammerdam, Redi and Malpighi proved the absurdity of the doctrine of spontaneous generation. Swammerdam, through his examination of countless small creatures, established the embryonic origin of insects as well. Francesco Redi of Arezzo, professor at Pisa, showed (1668) in his *Researches Regarding the Generation of Insects* that fecundated female insects lay eggs out of which the young are developed. He proved completely that meat maggots come from flies' eggs. For when he surrounded the meat with a fine gauze and prevented the flies from laying the eggs, the meat remained free of maggots. Experiments of this kind were ingenious forward thrusts into unknown realms of life, in which the intellectually wide-awake world took a passionate interest.

The third in this great triumvirate who, independently of each other, toilsomely extorted from the egg the knowledge of the generation of life, was Marcello Malpighi, professor in Bologna. Science has him to thank for the discovery of the chicken as a subject of research; from that time forth it became the most important helper in the unriddling of life's evolutionary processes.

Every six hours Malpighi opened an egg, and thus was the first to observe connectedly the embryonic development of a higher animal in the most distinctive stages of its evolution, and to picture and describe these stages in his book, *De Formatione Pulli* (1687). The professors of the then deteriorated, once so influential University of Bologna attacked his microscopic studies, first with scorn, then with hatred. He no longer dared to let himself be seen on the street. His house was stormed, his instruments were smashed, his manuscript was burned, his life threatened. Only a call to Rome ended these persecutions.

The forward step is tremendous. As the astronomical discoveries created a cosmic unity, an organized world system, so now is the way opened for an organized life system, an inner unity of all living things. From these revolutionary biological discoveries a straight road leads to the social and political revolutions of mankind. Since man has found the place where he stands in the universe, he must go to work on it now and set in order his family relations and the social functions of reciprocity.

As soon as the historian succeeds in thinking, not in years but in generations, historical space is shortened into a unified and grandiose march of evolution, in which the tragic and frightful errors of mankind appear more understandable and more pardonable. A hundred years are a fairly brief time for the completion of a historical reaction.

Swammerdam destroyed the false doctrine of spontaneous generation, but he created the false doctrine of preformation, the unfolding or emergence of already existing parts: a wrong hypothesis which corresponded so closely with the general views of the time that the leading minds helped it to prevail.

The first half of the eighteenth century was full of more or less successful attempts to arrive at a scientific system. In systematic natural history great things doubtless were accomplished. After such abundant harvests as the fifteenth or seventeenth century had brought forth, came the great period of the encyclopedists to stow away the crops in the barns of science. Here we need to recall only Linnaeus's *Systema Naturae*. But the transplanting of this gigantic yet wholly chaotic and incomplete new knowledge brought practical medicine into a truly pitiable state. Out of reasonable regulations grew a paranoic mass-epidemic, a system craze, that distracted men's brains and allowed patients to die.

It is a misfortune that theories in medicine are automatically converted into prescriptions. A star whose movement is falsely interpreted does not fall from the skies; a machine built on false plans simply stands still; but a sick man, when treated under a false system, is placed in peril of his life.

There were natural-born doctors in this century, of course, but they were either fanatical enemies of every theory like the Englishman, Thomas Sydenham (1624–1689), whose motto was "Experience, not reason, is what teaches"—a typical master of the healing art for all time, who well deserved the title of honor, an "English Hippocrates"—or they adopted a method like that of the famous Boerhaave of Leyden, who knew enough to keep his theories entirely separate from his practise.

The others—Helmont, Sylvius, Stahl's animism, Cullen, Stoll's gastric theory, Kämpf, Reil, Brown and many others whom it is needless to mention—caused nameless suffering and abundantly justified the adoption of unusual methods such as the homeopathy of Hahnemann. The worst is yet to come—the medical methods based on the speculations of natural philosophy.

The call for help issuing from that conscientious physician, A. F. Hecker, throws light on the situation at that time:

"The delusion of absolute perfection has been the pest of medicine from the beginning. How dare we conceal from ourselves that there are still innumerable things which we do not know? We still have no physiology! We know not what illness is, how medicine acts, how the ill are cured. . . . With new words and phrases, with metaphysical propositions, with chemical and dynamical hypotheses, with dialectics and disputations, with oratorical arts—and abusive words—we have made many disastrous attempts in the last two thousand years. Before all, let us see to it that we fill up the gaps and holes in our knowledge with a new vocabulary! . . . The confusion of speech in medicine has reached the limit. We have really come to the point where two physicians cannot discuss a point in their profession without first coming to an understanding on words and meanings."

This was written in 1805. Such was medical practise. The voices that would substitute facts for phantoms had to go unheard. Wolff lived a hundred years too soon.

Swammerdam, who out of the larva could conjure forth the compressed body of the unborn insect, was forced to the conclusion that in the maturing of the individual no really new development took place, but that growth was merely the unfolding of the smallest parts, the spreading out of intertwined, precreated parts. His sensitive hands simply completed the process of nature beforehand by force.

In Leibniz this theory of unfolding found its philosophical support. For him, mind and body form an ever indivisible partnership, the individual, the "monad." In the pursuit of his monad theory he arrives at this conclusion:

"The philosophers have made many difficulties for themselves over the origin of forms, intellects or souls. Meanwhile, careful researches with plants, insects and animals have led to the conclusion that the organic body never proceeds from a chaos or from decomposing matter, but always from buds or germs in which, without doubt, a preformation was present. Thus it has been determined that in this way not only does the organic body exist before generation, but also the soul in this body." In one part of his *Theodicy* he refers for support expressly to Leeuwenhoek's microscope: "So I am to understand that the souls, which are some day to be human souls, are present there in the seed; that they have existed in ancestors back to Adam, therefore since the beginning of things, always in the form of organized bodies."

Here for the first time we have a bold attempt to reconcile the biblical account of creation with the findings of science. Haller follows up this thought with mathematical exactitude. In his *Elements of Physiology* he asserts the existence of the horns in the newborn stag, of the beard in the boy. Beginning by accepting the view that earth and man have existed six thousand years, and taking a thirty-years cross-section of life and a head-count of a thousand million men alive at any given time, he figures out that when God created man in six days He created at least two hundred billion men at once! "There is no epigenesis!" is the proud battlecry of his book. "No part of an animal body is created before the others: all are created at the same time."

That Haller, who exercised unlimited authority in the realm of natural science, stuck so passionately to the unfolding theory was due to the sensational researches of Bonnet, who in 1745 discovered the virgin generation (parthenogenesis) of the plant louse. A hermetically segregated plant louse, in spite of complete virginity, on the eleventh day brought forth a living daughter, and in the next twenty days ninety-four more daughters, all of which in their turn bore progeny under the same conditions.

With that the theory of the unfolding of parts already present seemed to be proved irrefutably. But not only that. Another cause of strife, which in connection with the generation theory deeply stirred men's souls, seemed to be cleared away: the battle between the ovists and the animalculists—the disturbing question whether the preformation of the human race had its home in Adam's body or in Eve's.

A student at Leyden, Johann Ham, later mayor of his home town of Arnheim, in 1677 had discovered the "semen animalculae." Soon Leeuwenhoek confirmed this discovery in various animals. It seemed easy, in the animated movements of the sperm cell, in its animal-like form of head, middle section and tail, to imagine the homunculus which only needed to reach the fertile soil of the egg to unfold into a complete human being. Many prominent scientists, especially the eminent Spallanzani, the model for one of E. T. A. Hoffmann's most attractive fiction characters, confessed to being animalculists.

Over against them stood the ranks of the ovulists,

represented by Haller, Bonnet and Leibniz, proclaiming the opinion that the egg was the true animal germ and that the sperm threads, by pressing in, only gave the impulse to the development of the egg, in which all future generations lie locked up. At the same time some wholly obscure notions prevailed in regard to the development and growth of the human egg. Swammerdam's student friend in Leyden, Regnier de Graaf, had recognized the ovary as the place where the human egg was formed. This development brought to an end a lively debate with Swammerdam, whose agitation he had to allay in Delft at the age of thirty-two. The follicles of the ovary, which still bear the name of Graaf today, were then regarded as the actual eggs. Not until 1828 did Baer succeed in discovering the human egg in its nest in the follicle.

Against this prevailing doctrine of an unfolding process Wolff was the first to set forth his theory of "epigenesis." He accepted as a fundamental procedure in the creation and growth of all organic beings, plants or animals, a complete rebuilding of the original germs inside the parent organism. In fact, Wolff's rigorous critical investigation had definitely refuted the then current theory of preformation. "In so doing he did a great thing and prepared the soil for a scientific evolutionary system in the present-day sense." (Waldeyer.)

Wolff sent his dissertation to Haller, who reviewed it in detail in the Göttingen *Anzeiger*. Haller was at that time fifty-two years old, a world-famous man, president of the Göttingen Academy. Year by year since 1757 the eight-volume edition of his monumental work, *Physiological Elements of the Human Body*, had been appearing, filled with scientific knowledge of astonishing value. But already the suffering of this sensitive and melancholy man, torn as he was by the conflict between heart and head, had begun. He had suddenly left his academic post, to the dismay of his fellow workers, in order to accept a position as salt director of the Bernese mines at Aigle and to dwell in the rural seclusion of his Swiss home. The conflict between reason and faith, on which Swammerdam had come to grief, was also troubling this gifted eclectic in natural science.

The controversy of the two opponents, Haller and Wolff, who soon entered into an extensive exchange of letters, remains a memorable document of human behavior; one such as we too seldom find in the history of intellectual conflicts. Even when, in the course of the year, their points of view became ever more widely separated, never did either depart from the level of the highest respect for the intellectual achievements and uprightness of the other. Haller's objections to Wolff's ideas were primarily of a religious nature. To him they rightly seemed to be a serious danger to his orthodox faith, which deduced the mystery of the invisible Being from the mystery of the creative act in the primeval time of Adam. Wolff answered in his letter of April 17, 1767: "Against the existence of a Divine Being nothing has happened even if organic bodies are created by natural forces and from natural causes, since these forces and causes themselves, like nature itself, require an originator just as much as do organic bodies."

Another touching passage from one of his letters to Haller may be cited. On October 6, 1766, he wrote: "As regards our controversy, I think thus: For me not more than for thee it is the *truth* that lies on the heart. Whether it be that organic bodies unfold out of the invisible into the visible state, or whether it be that they grow and develop out of air: there is no reason why I should wish this more than that, or much more desire that and not desire this. Only the *truth* do we both seek; *that which is true* is our quest. Why, then, should I strive against thee, when thou strivest along with me toward the same goal? To thy care I entrust my epigenesis in full confidence that it will be defended and enlarged if it be true; and if it be false, I also shall hate it. I shall admire preformation if it be true, and will honor the adorable Originator of nature with the humblest devotion as a divinity inexplicable to human insight; but if it be false, thou wilt spurn it without hesitation, even if I be silent."

Wolff has later been designated, altogether wrongly, as a forerunner of monism. (E. Haeckel, *Anthropogenie*.) Philosophically he was an adherent of animism. The soulless materialism of the intromechanistic trend, as expressed in especially crass form in the contemporary work of Mettries, *L'Homme Machine*, was offensive to him and called forth his sharpest words. His enthusiastic disciple, Haeckel, wrote in 1903: "This [Wolff's] theory of epigenesis can scarcely be any longer called a theory today, since we have become fully convinced of the facts and can demonstrate them any moment with the help of the microscope."

Today, being in possession of the chromosome doctrine and of the first attempts at an exact science of inherited traits, we know that the preformation theory, even though in a very attenuated form, is again debatable. Every theory has its inner value as a working hypothesis. But again and again we fall into the danger that this unstable and often in the truest sense romantic theory, under the suggestion of its momentary power of persuasion, will be misused as a substitute for metaphysical realities. Our textbooks on physiology still say: "The first living beings must indeed have arisen through spontaneous generation (generatio aequivoca), that is, the coming into being of living substance out of inanimate matter; at present, however, so far as we know, there is no more spontaneous generation." (Schenck and Gürber, *Physiology of Man*.)

The outposts of knowledge are shifted. Nothing more. The latest discoveries of natural science make our understanding of the universe not easier, but harder. Knowledge can never take the place of piety, as the human mongrel sometimes arrogantly and foolishly asserts. Goethe alludes to the loss of ideals that accompanies every great discovery. For us technicians, machinists and constructors the arrogance of the early rationalistic era has vanished. Nowhere is the viewpoint of today's exact physics characterized more clearly and impressively than in the words of Werner Heisenberg, winner of the Nobel prize in physics for the year 1933:

"Almost every forward step in knowledge is bought with a renunciation. For almost every new perception we have to sacrifice earlier ideals and accepted solutions of important questions. With every great discovery— and this can be seen especially in modern physics—the pretensions of the scientist grow smaller so far as explaining the universe is concerned."

Kaspar Friedrich Wolff's labors were interrupted by military service. Frederick II was in a dubious situation. In October, 1760, the Russians were in Berlin. Prussia seemed to be helplessly abandoned to the invasion of its enemies. Then at the beginning of the year the Empress Elizabeth of Russia died, and her successor, Peter III, an admirer of Frederick, supported Prussia. Schweidnitz was won back.

During this period Wolff was giving lectures on anatomy to the young physicians of the army in the field hospital at Breslau. Frederick's physician in ordinary, Cothenius, organizer of the Prussian army sanitary corps, recognized the talent and ability of the young savant. Here also Wolff became acquainted with his true friend Mursina, who at that time, as a seventeen-year-old, had run away from a barber shop in Stolp. To the information which he gave to Goethe we owe the meager biographical data that we possess concerning Wolff's life. After the peace of Hubertusburg the hospitals were disbanded, and Wolff found himself back in Berlin, breadless and workless, in his father's tailor shop. Then he turned to his friend Cothenius, who was a prominent member of the faculty in the Medico-Surgical College, asking him to obtain permission for Wolff to give public lectures on physiology in Berlin.

One gets a clear conception of the power of the professorial clique when one follows the vain efforts of the influential Cothenius to obtain for his protégé a chance to make a living. The middle-class college remained closed to him. With great difficulty he obtained permission to deliver private lectures. Use of the apparatus, however, was refused; he was forbidden to enter the anatomy theater. His friend and admirer Mursina distributed the tickets with the announcement of his lectures. A rented hall was soon filled to overflowing. The students thronged the space before his improvised professorial chair. Wolff lectured on logic, on pathology, and especially on therapy. In 1764 his hearers had the benefit of a German version of his theory of generation. At his father's house, however, the hens are cackling. Every quarter of an hour an egg is broken open and the growth of the embryo is carefully observed under the microscope.

The results of Wolff's physiological heresies threw the professors into a white rage. The elder Meckel and the elder Walter hurled veritable curses of excommunication at him. Between the followers of Wolff and those of the schools the conflict developed into regular street battles. The prospect of Wolff's getting any official position grew steadily less. Then, in 1667, as we are told by the physicist Leonhard Euler, he received a call to the St. Petersburg Academy of Catherine II. The offer was not particuarly dazzling: 800 rubels a year, 200 rubels for traveling expenses, permanent assurance of a home and of practical activity. But, after the failure of a final attempt to obtain a professorship that had fallen vacant at home, no other choice remained. He married "a poor but beautiful girl," a brave Berliner, and set out in April, 1767, on his long journey.

The results of Wolff's private scientific work appeared a year later (1768) in the *Novi Commentarii* of the St. Petersburg Academy in the Latin language. They are still more valuable in essential content than the *Theory of Generation*. Ernst von Baer calls this work—*Concerning the Formation of the Intestinal Canal in the Hatched Chicken*—"the greatest masterpiece that we know of in the field of natural-scientific observation."

Despite the still wholly inadequate technical and other facilities for attaining knowledge in his time, Wolff gives in this work an almost faultless description of the development of the embryo out of the leaflike structures.

This achievement is like that of Servetus in describing the minor blood circuit, which was completed sixty years later by Harvey. Wolff was followed after fifty years by the completed bud-leaf theory of Pander, the Würzburg fellow worker of K. E. von Baer. Wolff showed the development of the chicken entrail from a leaf-shaped layer into a channel, then into a curving tube, then into a canal at whose ends the mouth and exit were formed.

"It appears that different systems of one and the

same type are formed at different times, one after the other, and that out of these a complete animal develops; and that these therefore are similar to each other, though in their essence they are different. The system that is generated first and is the first to take on an individual form, is the nervous system. When this is completed, the flesh is formed according to its type. Thereupon a third, the vascular system, appears. This is followed by a fourth, the alimentary canal, which again is built on the same model and appears to be a complete, self-contained whole like the first three."

We actually find a distinct anticipation of the cell theory in Wolff's work, as he recognized little, microscopically minute bubbles as the elementary materials out of which the embryonic layers are formed.

With the journey to Russia the curtain falls on the Wolff drama so far as European science is concerned. He was so completely forgotten that when in 1806 the well-known physicist Lorenz Oken, founder of the Natural Science Association, published his study, *Concerning the Development of the Intestine of the Chicken,* it contained not a single mention of the works of Wolff written long before. For twenty-seven years Wolff led the life of a learned bee in a little suburb of St. Petersburg, until an apoplectic stroke took the pen from his hand on February 22, 1794.

In 1812 Johann Friedrich Meckel, grandson of

Wolff's anatomy teacher, translated the book on the formation of the alimentary canal into German. Its appearance caused a small sensation. The copious introduction is an almost unique polemic against Oken.

Now the evolution of the evolutionary theory began its stormy course. Baer discovered the ovum (1827), Schleiden the vegetable cell (1838), Schwann the animal cell (1839). Robert Remak studied the embryonic structure of tissue (1851), and then came the endless chain of startling and brilliant discoveries, from Darwin to Mendel, from Spencer to Weismann, Loeb and Morgan, on whose foundations the still unfinished structure of evolutionary science and the science of inherited traits is being reared.

Time has finally overtaken the overhasty Berliner, Kaspar Friedrich Wolff, who at the age of twenty-six tried to leap over a generation and therefore had to stand on the spot for twenty-seven years.

The deep secret of the origin of man is today becoming a little more definitely known than it was two hundred years ago, but the miracle has become greater, more unimaginable and tremendous, and one's reverence in the presence of that miracle has grown no less.

JEAN DE LAMARCK

Founder of the Theory of the Evolutionary Origin of Species

VI

JEAN DE LAMARCK

*Founder of the Theory of the Evolutionary
Origin of Species*

THE French army under Marshal de Broglie and
Prince de Soubise stands facing the troops of Duke
Ferdinand of Brunswick in the neighborhood of Lipp-
stadt on July 15, 1761, when its outposts are approached
by a very ragged and unkempt young man accompanied by a still more wretched country youth. His horse
is almost collapsing from exhaustion and hunger. He
demands energetically to be conducted to Colonel de
Lastic, so that he may deliver a letter to him. The
colonel curses his friend Mme. de Lameth, an old lady
in the provinces, who, on the eve of a great battle, has
saddled him with this boyish Don Quixote. But he
gives the young man food and drink, and lets him
sleep in his bed.

Jean Baptiste Pierre Antoine de Monet, Chevalier
de Lamarck, looks much younger than his seventeen
years. He is the eleventh child of a poor country squire

in Bazentin, Picardy. All his ancestors and all his brothers have been officers. Jean, the youngest, coming too late and proving too weakly, is sent to the Jesuits at Amiens. His brothers tease the "little abbé" when they come home on furlough in their handsome uniforms. The eldest falls at the siege of Bergen-op-Zoom. The father dies. Jean de Lamarck runs away. His inheritance is just enough to buy a miserable nag. With a recommendation from the lady of the manor to the regiment of Beaujolais, he lays the broad road behind him in double-quick time and reaches the army at a critical moment.

Lastic has to go to headquarters to receive the latest orders. In the gray dawn of the morning, when he takes his place at the head of his regiment, he discovers between his bearded grenadiers—in the front rank—the lean runaway from Picardy!

"What are you doing here?" he yells at him. "You have no business here. Get out, and be lively about it."

"I am here to serve, Colonel."

It is no time for disputes or explanations. Lamarck remains. His regiment takes up its position in a hollow. Soon the captain's skull is shattered. Then the lieutenant falls. One after another, the men are struck down. After a few hours only fourteen remain. The French have to retreat. Lamarck and his comrades realize that they have been completely forgotten. The old soldiers ask the self-possessed youth to take over the command.

"Comrades," he says, "we have been stationed here, and we cannot leave without orders. If you are afraid, go. I stay."

The scattered little band lay down and waited, while the enemy pressed in around them. Meanwhile the colonel had noted the loss of his company. In the face of great danger an officer crept to the lost post.

"Now we can go," cried Lamarck; "now we have orders." *

Colonel de Lastic is in raptures over his young hero. He takes him that same evening to the marshal, who promotes him to a position as officer.

Thus began Lamarck's career as a soldier. He became a collector of plants and a writer of books, but the glorious upswing of that youthful episode throws light upon his whole character and career. The founder of the theory of descent by evolution, the discoverer of lines of thought which still stir mankind in unexampled fashion, was one of the noblest and most talented amateurs ever known. Wherever he was placed, he achieved great things with his passionate will to work and fulfil his duty. An almost superhuman soldier, he defended a far-outlying, lost outpost of science sur-

* This information is taken from a letter written by Lamarck's son to Cuvier on February 20, 1830. Published by J. T. Hamy, *Les Débuts de Lamarck*, etc. Bibliothèque d'Histoire Scientifique. Vol. 2.

rounded by enemies. When a later generation advanced to that place, he had long been lying in a poor man's nameless grave. He had created the word "biology," and thereby had done much more than coin a clever name. It is through Lamarck that the "science of life" obtained its fundamental form and aim. No professional "expert" could accomplish that. The motive of his work was the psychical adventure of creation, and the thing created arose out of the poetic sense. Out of Lamarck, the soldier, the thinker, the advocate of order and exactness, came scientific research as we know it today. Biology as a social science, as the dramatic doctrine of the destiny of mankind, traces its beginning back to him.

The Jesuit pupil becomes an officer. The officer becomes a doctor of medicine. The medical doctor becomes a botanist. The botanist becomes a meteorologist. The meteorologist becomes a chemist. The chemist becomes a zoologist. The zoologist becomes a philosopher. Where he camouflages as an expert, he is willingly and gladly recognized. Where he deals with ideals, he is regarded as a poor fool.

It is difficult, in the case of Lamarck, to discover adequate grounds for the hostility of fate toward him; from the viewpoint of the historical psychologist, however, they would be worth knowing. His life was altogether too unfavorably placed. The sunshine and rain which his period poured into a life always came to him at the wrong moment, so that he could seldom harvest his crop. From the expiring glory of absolutism under Louis XV, through the earthquake of the Revolution to the rise and fall of Bonapartism, and from there to the clerical-royalist plutocracy of the Bourbon restoration under Louis XVIII is a long way. It requires the iron discipline of a soldier to complete this march as a man of intellect and genius without becoming a minister of state or being beheaded. For his great contemporaries it turned out otherwise.

Lavoisier at the age of twenty-seven (1770), through his law of the conservation of matter—"In chemical processes nothing new is created and nothing vanishes: the sum of the materials entering into the process is an unchangeable quantity"—had not only laid the foundations for the powerful development of chemistry, but also discovered a fundamental biological principle. He still had twenty-four years in which to create the physiology of breathing in an extraordinary and brilliant series of experiments and researches, and to win the final victory over the then generally discredited phlogiston idea, the speculative flame-matter invented by Georg Ernst Stahl. Then the grand seignior and farmer-general of the tobacco administration, the partizan of corruption and exploitation of misery, on May 8, 1794, at the command of Robespierre, had to mount the scaffold. To the last minute he went on working in his prison upon his *Memoirs of Physics and Chemistry*. In vain did influential men who had not lost their senses—the physicist Coulomb, the mathematician Lagrange—try to save this irreplaceable life for the nation; the unproved charge that he had added water to the tobacco outweighed their pleas. Coffinhal, president of the revolutionary tribunal, coined the famous expression, "Justice must take its course; we have no use for any more men of learning." So ended Lavoisier at the age of fifty-one. The voice of Saint-Just resounds through this year: "The palate of the French people is dulled like that of a drunkard. Death has lost its terrors. This is a desert place in life."

Men of learning, however, were soon needed. The victory of the Convention over the mad roar for blood on 9th Thermidor of the year IV drove the first free wave of confidence over the land. The termites of the spirit pulled the ruins together and began forthwith to build again where the receding flood had allowed solid ground to appear. In this favorable climate the aging Lamarck also found shelter. Along with the twenty-one-year-old Geoffroy Saint-Hilaire he became a professor in the newly founded Museum of Natural History.

Geoffroy had good fortune. Revolutions always make men favor boys. The beautiful saying of his teacher

Daubenton deserves to be remembered: "I take upon myself the responsibility for your inexperience. Go ahead and take over the instruction in zoology, and some day it can be said that you have made a French science of it." Geoffroy honorably fulfilled this commission.

Lamarck's most important contemporary opponent, Cuvier, also belonged to this fortunate post-revolutionary generation. He was twenty-five years younger than Lamarck. His "catastrophe theory," that the earth perishes every few thousand years and is created anew, gave the biblical story of the creation a further claim on life and was well adapted to the uses of a reactionary clerical régime in which he climbed to the highest honors and offices. He became general inspector of public instruction, a peer of France, while Lamarck, his fatherly friend and patron of earlier days, wasted away in blindness and poverty.

The climax of this earthly injustice, however, was the "eulogy" on Lamarck which Cuvier delivered at the public session of the Academy on November 26, 1832, after his death. In this strangest of funeral orations the honored and prosperous originator of the catastrophe theory inflicted upon Lamarck, who could no longer defend himself, a sort of scientific degradation by holding up his great and true ideas to pitying ridicule. Such shameful dramas are exceedingly instructive.

Finally Darwin, the gifted finisher of Lamarck's theory of descent, came along fifty-eight years later and was able to achieve an immediate and sensational success with his *Origin of Species* (1859). This book was sold out on the first day. It was quickly translated into all the languages of the world. It immediately stirred up a movement of worldwide character, "Darwinism," whose excesses made a great deal of trouble for serious natural science.

Of course, Darwin also had to contend with powerful opposition, and the hostility of orthodox theologians led from the speech of the Oxford-educated Bishop Wilberforce, who scornfully asked Darwin's famous disciple Thomas H. Huxley whether it was on his grandfather's or his grandmother's side that he had descended from the apes, all the way down to the "monkey trial" of 1925 in Dayton, Tennessee, through a series of scandals more comic than tragic. But the Victorian Age, which knew how to unite the progress of civilization so fruitfully with political conservatism, could and did grow spontaneously enthusiastic over Darwin's numerous and easily understood facts and proofs, over his fundamentally optimistic theses of "artificial selection" and the "survival of the fittest races in the struggle for life," expanded—in terms comprehensible to the most primitive mentality—into a favorable forecast for the future of mankind.

Darwin, however, did not wish to know much about his intellectual predecessor, Lamarck; with all respect for the hermit of Down, this must be noted. For him Lamarck was only one of the many earlier gropers after evolution, among whom he regarded Plato, Buffon and his grandfather Erasmus Darwin as far more important than Lamarck. To his friend Lyell, the founder of geology and an admirer of Lamarck, he wrote on March 12, 1863: "Between the *Origin of Species* and Lamarck's book I can see nothing in common . . . a book which, after two deliberate readings, I regard as wretched, and out of which I have obtained nothing." He expressed himself in the same way to Hooker. In his works he scarcely mentions Lamarck.

One must know a man's environment in order to be aware of the peculiar circumstances upon which his acts often depend. These anecdotic incidents can be regarded as freaks of fate quite as easily as they can be taken for leadings of divine providence. One thing is sure: as soon as one releases one's heroes from all judgments regarding individual luck, fame, power and enjoyment, even the most foolish martyrdom takes on a truly godlike aspect and assumes a well ordered place in the social progress of our surveyable historical epoch, which at longest does not yet reach back a hundred generations. How it will all turn out, frankly, we do not know.

Cuvier, in his "eulogy," blames Lamarck with errors. Certainly, Lamarck erred often and seriously. But Cuvier's error, his theory of catastrophes, was a case of jumping off the track to uphold other errors. Lamarck's erroneous opinions belonged, at least predominantly, in the category of the blessed, gifted, creative errors which for mankind are just as significant as truth. Even the invention of an error can be an element of creative power; yes, the direct forerunner of a truth that is to be found. There are no great men in whose work error does not play a part, often an important part. And it is foolish and far too customary to excuse one's own shortcomings by the exposure of such errors in greater men.

After the close of the Seven Years' War, Lieutenant Lamarck remained with his regiment for five years doing garrison work at Toulon and Monaco. At the latter place he was wounded one day in the neck. The injury would not heal. He went to Paris and was treated by the surgeon, Dr. Tenon. Deep scars remained. He was through with military service. During his stay in the South he had busied himself with a collection of plants arranged according to a botanical book which his brother, on leave of absence, had stuck into his pocket in exchange for some notebooks. With the help of an apothecary he arranged his first herbarium.

Lamarck settled in Paris with a "maintenance pension" of 400 francs. It amounted to starving. But he was only twenty-three years old, so he went into the banking business as an apprentice. For almost a year he added up figures for M. de Bout in the Rue Thévenot. During this time he lived in an attic room of a house on Mont Sainte-Geneviève. From his window he could see nothing but clouds. Through Lamarck this dreamy outlook became the beginning of meteorology. He began to separate the cloud forms from each other, and gave each a name—cirrus, cumulus, stratus, nimbus—to which we are still accustomed today. He believed he could detect close relations between the cloud forms and the weather, of whose predictability he was convinced.

In later life Lamarck published his weather observations from 1799 to 1810 in a *Meteorological Year Book*. They brought him plenty of ridicule. No one was able to comprehend this serious though necessarily inadequate attempt at a science which was destined to remain in uncertainty for another century. A scene between Napoleon and Lamarck ended this undertaking, on which Lamarck had set his heart. The physicist Arago, as an eye-witness, has described this encounter:

Napoleon, in the Tuileries, is receiving the honorary societies. Among the members of the Institute
stands the sixty-six-year-old Lamarck holding a book
in his hand for the emperor. "Is that some of your
absurd meteorology," snaps Napoleon; "the year book
that is a disgrace to one of your age? Concern yourself
with natural history, then I will accept your books with
pleasure. I will take this volume only out of respect
for your gray hair." After these rude and cutting words
of the emperor, poor Lamarck tried in vain to say, "But
it is indeed a natural history which I hold here in my
hand." He burst into tears.

In the first years of his Paris sojourn Lamarck hesitated between the study of music and that of medicine.
His brother persuaded him to choose medicine, and
at the age of twenty-four he began his studies. Soon,
however, he was a constant visitor at the botany lectures
in the Royal Gardens. Into these ten years of intensive
study fall his meetings with Rousseau, who during his
stay in Paris at that time enjoyed botanizing on Mont
Valérian behind St. Cloud. These excursions were performed with peculiar rites. Among the most important
preliminary requirements for permission to join them
was that nobody should ask questions and nobody
should look at Rousseau; otherwise he would at once
take flight and leave his pupils on the spot.

In 1778 Lamarck's first great work appeared, a

three-volume description of the French flora, which long remained the standard botany. Buffon saw the manuscript and was enthusiastic over it. Through him the work was published at government expense in the royal printing office, and through his influence Lamarck was elected to the Academy of Sciences the next year. The French Flora was a great success. Rousseau had made the study of flowers and plants very fashionable, and Parisian society was fully prepared to prize a book published under official patronage. Lamarck appeared again to be facing a brilliant career.

He took courage and placed before the Academy a manuscript, *Researches on the Chief Physical Phenomena,* which he had already completed in 1776. This manuscript acted like cold lightning. In the Academy Lavoisier ruled. As soon as this ponderous body, with unspeakable pains, had changed its way of thinking and allowed itself to be converted to the foolish doctrine of phlogiston, up rose this beginner and climber and swore also by that out-of-date phlogiston. Lamarck stood there, branded as an apostate, bowed beneath the hatred of the whole Academy, and this hatred was to pursue him all the rest of his life; it outlasted the Revolution and the empire. In the eyes of the Academy Lamarck remained a dilettante. A commission was appointed to report on the manuscript. It preferred to say nothing, and Lamarck took back his manuscript.

But after sixteen years, being obstinate, he utilized the climax of political catastrophe and confusion (1794) to publish this dubious work, "dedicated to the French people." He had never recognized Lavoisier and Priestley.

He was still in Buffon's good graces, however, and Buffon sent him in 1781 with his son on a long journey, under a royal commission, to establish connections with the chief botanical gardens of Europe. On this useful trip Lamarck visited Holland, Vienna, Hungary, Berlin—where he established relations with Gleditsch—and Göttingen. He came back laden with mineral and plant treasures. In 1783 he was named as a fellow worker with Diderot and d'Alembert on the systematic *Encyclopedia* which they had begun. In 1785 appeared the first volume of his *Dictionary of Botany,* the beginning of that mammoth work in which, in the course of twenty-five years, he described the plants from A to P, a gigantic and brilliantly executed undertaking.

In 1788, at the age of forty-four, Lamarck was able for the first time in his life to obtain a position. Through the death of Buffon a minor post as conservator of the royal herbarium was left vacant. But the very next year this wretched office was made precarious by all sorts of intrigue. He had to defend his meager foothold on life with tooth and nail, drafting memorials and writing letters of entreaty. He drew up a plan for the thorough reorganization of the Garden of Plants into a Museum of Natural History. In 1791 Bernardin de Saint-Pierre, author of *Paul and Virginia* and anything but a scholar, was put under his nose.

The death of Louis XVI and the triumph of the Revolution brought Lamarck release from his ten years' misery. The Constitutent Assembly finally approved the museum project. But before Lamarck was aware of it all the professorships were taken. The three botanists would not yield; over the rocks Daubenton presided; young Geoffroy Saint-Hilaire had the higher animals; Lacépède was an expert on reptiles and fishes. There remained only the insects and worms of Linnæus. The botanist Lamarck decided to take over these. In the first budget of the new undertaking he is registered: "Lamarck, fifty years, second time married; wife pregnant; six children; professor of the zoology of insects, worms, and the lower forms of life. Salary, 2868 livres, 6 sous, 8 deniers."

Lamarck attacked the study of zoology like a soldier attacking an enemy of superior strength. After a year's preparation he began his lectures on April 30, 1796. The Revolution lay at the last gasp. The Convention had been followed by the Directory, which made desperate efforts to avert the ruin now impending, and swept up the assignat rubbish. Baboeuf, the last camp-follower of the revolutionary idealism, after an unsuccessful uprising, drove a dagger into his breast before he could be executed. Lamarck, however, with dictatorial power brought order into the farthest corner of the animal world, the 354th family in the Linnæan system, which up to that time had to be content with the simple designation of "chaos."

What Lamarck here accomplished with extraordinary labor in a brief time was generously recognized. He began with the happy division of the animal world into vertebrate and invertebrate. The army of the invertebrates, now under his command, in the next ten years took on an ever more significant and exact form. In the year 1807 its division into ten classes was completed: (1) mollusks, (2) cephalopods, (3) annelidae, (4) crustaceae, (5) arachnidae, (6) insects, (7) worms, (8) radiates, (9) polyps, (10) infusoria. This division fixed in all essential points the famous classification of Cuvier. In the seven volumes of his *Natural History of Invertebrate Animals,* published between 1815 and 1822, Lamarck, already going blind, gave himself up to his zoological researches to the last limit of his physical strength.

Out of this grew the strange circumstance that Lamarck is generally regarded as a prominent zoologist but a crazy philosopher. For him, however, the systematizing of the animal world was only a preliminary to the vast cosmogony which played an ever more dominant rôle in his thoughts. None of his contemporaries had the slightest intimation that his "dilettantism," his vagabonding into remote realms, the centrifugal mania that drove him forth from the place of his researches, was the expression of a strong determination to understand the plan of the created world. With the sovereign stoicism that characterized him, he endured the severest humiliations and illnesses, of both of which there were not a few. His meteorological studies, his *Hydrogeology,* published in 1802, were for him important preliminary steps toward knowing the laws under which the earth was formed, for on these laws, above all, he already felt certain, depended the formation and evolution of living bodies. Much in his theory was wrong, but this in no wise justified the arrogance of his opponents, whose theories were no nearer to being right. The decisive fact is that his studies in physics and geology smoothed the way for the great discoveries of his chief work, published in 1809—his *Zoological Philosophy,* the first attempt at a "general biology" in the spirit of modern natural science.

Of what does this fundamental doctrine of Lamarck consist? For decades he had been tirelessly describing and classifying plants and animals. Every enthusiastic collector becomes a fanatic on deviations from type.

But he also classified these variations and discovered in their permanence three kinds of conformity with law. Lamarck was certain of the unity of the animal kingdom; he destroyed the old faith in the constancy of species; for him a gradual evolution from lower to higher—in an ascending scale and in unlimited periods of time—was proved to be under way through the alteration of species. And likewise he believed he had discovered in the changing conditions of the physical world the mechanism by which species were changed. On this score Lamarck becomes the founder of the theory of evolutionary descent, under whose jurisdiction, in increasing measure, we live today.

However extensive the alterations and deepenings may be which the later scientists, especially Darwin, have wrought upon this genius-thought, its central truth and its overwhelming significance become ever more apparent. Individual scientists have often believed they were delivering the final blow to the theory of evolutionary descent, but at best they have hit nothing but its more vulnerable offspring, Darwinism. The modern science of genetics, in the storm-and-stress period at the turn of the last century, often believed it had completely refuted the theory of evolution; yet it was compelled, the deeper and more astonishing our knowledge became, to go back to it.

Apropos of the coincidence of great thoughts, it is

decidedly interesting to note that Goethe, without having known Lamarck, separately—though without thorough confirmation—advocated the theory of descent with astonishing clarity; the idea, indeed, lay at the base of his theory of the metamorphoses of plants. He says: "An inner and primal unity lies at the base of all organic life; the deviation from type arises out of the necessary correlative relations with the outer world, and from this we have a right to deduce a primal and corresponding deviation and a constantly progressing transformation, in order to be able to comprehend phenomena that are as constant as they are variable." In another place: "Everything that Nature desires to make she must make through a series. She indulges in no leaps. She cannot create a horse, for example, unless it is preceded by all the other animals, upon which, as upon a ladder, she climbs to the structure of the horse." In Lamarck we read: "The species of the genera, arranged in a series and set side by side according to their correlative forms, differ so slightly from their next neighbors that all gradations are available and these species to a certain extent melt into each other. . . . How then can one fix one's eyes upon the peculiar scale that exists in the systematic arrangement of animals, if one runs through them in order from the most complete to the least complete, without inquiring, 'Upon what can so positive and extraordinary

a fact, confirmed to me by so many proofs, depend?
. . . Shall I not think that Nature has made the different living bodies successively as she advanced from
the simplest to the most complex?' "

The thesis of Lamarck that provoked the most
strife was that of adaptation. "It is not the organs, that
is, the forms and peculiarities of the parts of the animal
body, which produce its habits and special characteristics, but on the contrary it is the animal's habits, its
mode of life and the surroundings amid which its ancestors lived, that have shaped its organs and its
characteristics."

Lamarck tried to prove this fundamental proposition
in part with very primitive means, which brought upon
him the scorn and laughter of his contemporaries. The
giraffe and the kangaroo were for him symbols of
adaptation, and he went so far as to believe that a
Cyclopean race could be created if people blind in one
eye were bred together long enough. But still more
foolish and banal were the objections of Cuvier when,
to prove the constancy of species, he cited the fact that
the mummied cats and ibises from ancient Egypt were
identical with the cats and ibises of the present day.
Lamarck could easily refute this pseudo-argument of
stability in an age when the first digging up of pre-
historic fossils gave more than a hint of the vast periods

of time that had elapsed while the changes on the earth's surface were taking place.

Through Lamarck's creative hypothesis of adaptation the problem of "inheritance of acquired characters" was for the first time injected into scientific discussion. However one may stand on this question, it is certain that it has made for the wider development of research; especially has it been richly fruitful in the formulation of questions of hereditary transmission. It cannot be said that the point has been decided. However convincing the breeding experiments of the present day may seem to be, and however much our more certain knowledge of the mechanism of hereditary transmission may appear to disprove the possibility of inheriting acquired characters, there is other experimental evidence that leads us to think quite otherwise; for instance, the recently established heritability of a darkening of the crystalline lens of rabbits as a result of artificial injuries to the eyes of their ancestors.

When one traces the historic fate of Lamarck's ideas through the brief span of time since they were launched, one encounters an absolutely dramatic dénouement which can be explained only by the deep metaphysical interest of mankind in these questions and the bitter warfare between myth and knowledge.

First of all, assaulted as they were by contemporary incompetence and insufficiency, his teachings were completely forgotten and buried as beneath a rubbish heap. The high tide of the speculations of the nature-philosophers broke in and threw all concepts into such complete disorder that in 1859 Darwin's *Origin of Species* had the effect, for many, of release from a labyrinth.

Darwin widened Lamarck's theory of descent in most fortunate fashion with his selection idea—the theory of natural selection. The superabundant increase of the animal world, its dependence on variability, according to Darwin, leads to a selective process through the "struggle for existence," in which the fittest survive and the unfit perish. Darwin established his thesis with an enormous fund of material proof in his main work and in those which followed—*Variation of Animals and Plants under Domestication* (1868), *The Descent of Man* (1871), *Expression of the Emotions in Men and Animals* (1872). The immediate favor with which his writings were received constitutes the first enormous and warning example of mass publicity for a scientific idea.

The masses were unprepared for this glimpse into a wholly strange and yet pertinent world of the structure of life, and they found it hard to bear. One sees how facts can stir up and befog a consciousness unaccustomed to them. The joining up of Darwin's revelation with the doctrine of political and social materialism degraded it into joyless propaganda material for the producing of a philosophic anarchy which at last endangered its own scientific value. Here again, in this decisive struggle for mental mastery of the coming twentieth century, the church did not have enough faith in its divine mission to see that every truth, however undogmatic, can serve for the strengthening and establishing of religious thought. It struggled fruitlessly to explain away undeniable principles for the sake of its myths, and thus it allowed the metaphysical forces of monism to go to waste in a banal atheistic and nationalistic movement which has done much to produce dangerous convulsions in the social structure.

It would have been well if, at the height of the Darwinian vogue, the creator of the theory of descent, Lamarck, had not been so completely forgotten. At the close of his *Zoological Philosophy* stands this deathless yet wholly forgotten sentence:

"Nature, this immeasurable collection of all the different beings and bodies, in all of whose parts there is going on an eternal round of movement and change that is governed by law—this totality, which alone is unchangeable so long as its supreme Originator is pleased to let it exist, must be regarded as a whole which is created out of its parts for a purpose known only to its Creator, and not exclusively for one of these parts. Since every part necessarily must be changed and cease to be, in order that another may thereby be created, it has interests opposed to the whole; and when the part judges the whole, it finds the whole badly made. Meanwhile, this whole is perfect and is fulfilling completely the purpose for which it was created."

This has nothing to do with the materialistic-monistic system that was built up under Haeckel's leadership. Germany became, mainly through Haeckel's temperament, the battleground of the Darwinian view of things. This double-track mind—this scholar and fanatic—achieved enormous things for the idea of evolution and did it measureless injury. His *General Morphology,* a book written as in a delirium in the brief space of a year and under the heavy blow of the loss of his first wife, is a magnificent attempt to present the whole range of evolutionary thought for all categories of life. In utter consistency he coined here his "fundamental principle of biogenetics": "Ontogeny is a shortened and incomplete recapitulation of philogeny"; that is, every man repeats in his embryonic life all the steps in the evolutionary history of the race. In spite of its questionable apodictic form, this hypothesis has proved to be especially helpful for the progress of science. It furnished the necessary bridge between Wolff and Lamarck, between embryology and family history.

A radical Darwinist of an entirely different sort was the Freiburg zoologist August Weismann, who was the first to seek to get the full value, along Darwinian lines, of the budding science of genetics through the discovery of the chromosomes in the cell-nucleus. In his book, *The All-Sufficiency of Natural Selection*, he came to the conclusion that "natural selection produces all species-adaptations." He went so far as to trace the "struggle for life" back to the germ cells, as he held that the chromosomes, the inheritance units, consist of numerous tiny parts with independent functions, and that in the narrow prison of the cell-nucleus there is the same deadly warfare between the stronger and the weaker elements of the germ plasm as in all the rest of nature. In fact, he established the truth of this brilliant speculative conception—in part, at least—since the existence of these infinitesimal elements, with the specific inheritance function of the chromosomes, was recently demonstrated by American scientists.

It must suffice here to mention very briefly the objection of the so-called Neo-Lamarckists, especially of the English philosopher Herbert Spencer, who once more very positively denied the "inheriting of acquired characters," since the functional adaptation of the whole organic system to the requirements of the surrounding world cannot be explained by natural selection. Weismann believed that, by means of his significant theory of the continuity of the germ plasm, he had finally proved the absurdity of the idea that acquired traits can be inherited so long as they affect only the body and do not reach the germ cells. After observing twenty-two successive generations of dogs whose tails were cut off, he stated that "among the 1592 young born of tailless parents there was not a single one with a tail in any way defective."

A fundamental revision of the theory of descent was brought about primarily by the new knowledge of hereditary transmission. The first results of this latter science seemed to contradict dogmatic Darwinism completely, and the downfall of Darwinism as a speculative system seemed to be assured. But at that moment came the necessary and wholesome reaction against philosophical Darwinism of the Haeckel stamp, which got its hardest blow from the metaphysics of Hans Dreisch, based on biology.

It is not our intention to mix in this fight. The opposition movement has the historical merit of having destroyed the monist miracle-belief in the "solving of the world riddle" and thereby of having removed the political propaganda value of Darwinism, at least in Germany. Behind the idea of descent rises the much greater thought of hereditary transmission, a thought

indissolubly bound up with it and far more pregnant
with results; one whose cultural importance and attrac-
tiveness throws into the shade everything that we were
accustomed to look for in the way of thought stimulus
in a scientific doctrine.

The high points in the researches on genetics are the
discovery of the process of fertilization, the discovery
of the chromosomes as bearers of the germ plasm, and
the finding of the laws of cross-breeding. In 1866 there
appeared in the *Discussions of the Natural Science Society of Brünn* the first information from Gregor
Mendel concerning his researches in the cross-breeding
of peas, from which he deduced with absolute clarity
the independent inheritance of individual characters
and the law of the splitting of inherited characters.
Forty separate statements were sent out, 120 scientific
societies received the discussions. But Mendel shared
the fate of Lamarck. He was no professional expert.
No one living with him shared the thrill of one of the
greatest discoveries ever made. Mendel soon afterward
became abbot of the royal monastery at Brünn and
had to give up his researches. His contemporary, Darwin, never heard his name. He died in 1884. Thirty-
four years after the appearance of his work, sixteen
years after his death, in 1900, Mendel's law was redis-

covered simultaneously and independently from each other by the Hollander de Vries, by the German Correns, and by the Austrian Tschermak. The pious Gregor Mendel's remark, "My time will yet come," was fulfilled.

The world's shameful oversight in this matter may be explained to some extent by the fact that at the time of Mendel's discovery the mechanics of hereditary transmission still lay wholly in the dark. In 1875 Oscar Hertwig took to experimenting in Messina with a new research animal, the sea urchin, and succeeded in tracing the process of fertilization and in stating its fundamental principles: "Fecundation depends upon the blending of sexually differentiated cells." In the following year Fol saw the spermatic filament penetrating the egg, that elementary act of creation which no one thus far had been able to observe. In the same year Van Beneden traced the various stages of development in the maturing of the egg. A little later, in 1879, Flemming was rejoiced to be able to prove the lengthwise splitting of the peculiar spermatic filaments already described by Hertwig, to which Waldeyer now gave the name "chromosomes." In 1885 Rabi established a definite numerical law for these chromosomes. There was no longer a doubt that the chromosomes are the carriers of heredity.

In the ten years from 1875 to 1885 all the existing principles governing the process of generation were discovered. Then Mendel's time had come. Mendelism and cell research have remained the foundations of the science of genetics.

Once more there arose a great opponent of the evolutionary idea in the Dane, Johannsen. The theory of descent finds one of its props in the heritability of race differences. On the evidence of extensive breeding experiments Johannsen now called attention to the differences between the phenomenal type (phenotype) and the normal inheritance type (genotype), which had become of great importance in researches in heredity. The outward appearance of an individual tells nothing concerning his inherited nature; the presence of hidden traits comes to light only in his offspring. There are inheritable variations (mutations) and uninheritable variations (fluctuations). These uninheritable fluctuations were now identified with Darwin's "individual variations," since men were convinced of the great rarity of the inheritable mutations. But, since uninheritable characters cannot be elements of a selection, Johannsen concluded that "Darwinism is finally refuted by the new variability and inheritance doctrine." Morgan and Baur, however, in certain experiments connected with their researches on breeding, found the supposedly rare mutations to be present in large numbers. The zoologist, William von Buddenbrock, ends a historical-biological survey with these words:

"Thus we have this surprising state of affairs: that genetics, which at first was regarded as the deadly enemy of Darwinism, in the end has become its confederate, while it has ensconced itself securely as the basis of the theory of natural selection. In its newest development it leads to a complete confirmation of Darwin's fundamental views and hypotheses." (R. Hertwig, 1927.)

"Nothing remains for us but to place Lamarck's name ahead of Darwin's."

In his last years Lamarck traveled through the Valley of the Shadow of Death. After 1818 his eyesight failed rapidly. The old man soon had to give up his professorship to his pupil, Latreille. And now began a painful leave-taking ten years long. Death played hide-and-seek with him. Three wives died, and four of his seven children. Two daughters, Cornelia and Rosalie, lived with him, shared his tasks, and when he was wholly blind they wrote from dictation the last two volumes of his *Natural History*. His daughter Cornelia remained constantly by his side. When her father could no longer leave his bed, she also left the house no more. The first time she went out after her father's death she fainted, because it was so long since she had felt the fresh air.

Lamarck was very poor. His slender savings had long ago vanished through speculations into which unscrupulous advisers had led him. His daughters were left without a pension. Martins, the publisher of the posthumous edition of the *Zoological Philosophy,* wrote:

"I myself saw Miss Cornelia de Lamarck in 1832 working for meager pay, mounting on white paper the plants of the herbarium in the museum where her father was once a professor."

Her touching words, "Posterity will admire you, it will avenge you, my father," are chiseled on the monument that was erected to Lamarck in 1909 in the Jardin des Plantes.

There is a portrait of him at the age of eighty in the uniform of a member of the Institute. He is here a man on the march between earth and heaven. Splendidly dressed, his coat adorned with golden scroll work, the furrow of bitterness diagonally across his face, the blind eyes strained keen-sightedly upon his goal, with high, upright brow and with head a little forward-leaning, he still looks more like a field marshal than like a scholar.

He died on December 18, 1829, at the age of eighty-five. On Montparnasse he was buried in the ranks of the poor, who every five years are driven out of their graves to make room for new arrivals. Lamarck's remains rest somewhere among the heaps of bones of his unknown brethren.

ROBERT MAYER

Discoverer of the Law of the Conservation of Energy

VII

ROBERT MAYER

Discoverer of the Law of the Conservation of Energy

IN THE cold night of February 11, 1840, a skiff
carried the ship's doctor, Julius Robert Mayer,
twenty-six-year-old son of the apothecary at the Sign
of the Rose, a native of the little town of Heilbronn on
the Neckar, out to the *Java,* which was to sail from
Rotterdam to Surabaya with 100,000 bricks.

Mayer, son of a well-to-do burgher, was born on
November 25, 1814. At the age of fifteen he went to
the evangelical theological seminary at Schönstadt, in
order to enter Tübingen University three years later as
a medical student. His first impressions of the great
world were gained in the sturdy, visionary world of the
30's, behind whose dreamy graciousness, which would
not let itself be dragged through the battle of rising
political passions, the tragic conflicts of the coming
century were beginning to trace their ghostly dawn.
Hailed joyously by European youth, the refugees of

the Polish rebellion move through Germany. In Paris, after the uprising of July, 1830, blooms the corrupt but intellectually efficient brilliancy of the "juste milieu." In Germany the national democratic movement is getting under way. The Hambach festival, the reaction, the German tariff union, that magnificent example of the professorial spirit, the "Göttingen Seven" (1837), the Kulturkampf in Prussia—these are the themes of student debate in a life flickering uncertainly between harmlessness and horror.

On account of taking part in a forbidden society in Tübingen, the Questphalia, Mayer was expelled. In prison he refused all food for six long days, until he was allowed to go home without having betrayed one of his comrades. This incident did not injure him much. He took a look at life in Vienna, Munich, Paris. His parents were horrified at his plan to journey to the East Indies. That appeared to them to be entirely too bold an extreme of the old Swabian love of wandering. But they gave way to their son's impetuosity.

Well supplied with letters of credit, he travels from France to Holland. "One can find nothing more romantic," he writes to his father (February 18, 1840), "than these railway journeys by night, when the fire in the engine often suddenly lights up the way, and other trains fly past with wheels glowing in the reflection."

It is a critical moment in which he is beginning his journey. The Prussian captain, Helmuth von Moltke, is shaping a modern army for Turkey in her war against Egypt. France is backing Egypt. Behind Turkey stands the Quadruple Alliance—Russia, England, Austria, Prussia. The French are arming against Germany. "Die Wacht am Rhein" is sung. Frederick William IV, on ascending the throne, honors Arndt and Jahn. Germany is on its way to become a nation. "It will be a fortunate thing for me," writes Mayer to his parents on July 25, 1840, "if peace holds out until our return."

In letters to his school friend Lang, Mayer had earlier painted on a larger scale the dangers of his journey into adventure, saying that "in Batavia at least half the newly arrived Europeans die within a year." But the wide world is now showing him the endless monotony of freedom. Salt meat, gin, fog and sunshine, fowl and fish, a sail on the horizon, the horse-play of an equatorial crossing, a grumbling captain and a none too peaceful crew. After an endless stretch of 101 days he observes with tears of relief that "there is still some land remaining on this planet." The three-master drops anchor at Batavia. From there it goes to the roads of Surabaya. Four months they remain in the East Indies, delivering the bricks and taking on sugar and coffee, until after almost a year's absence the *Java* is back again in Rotterdam early in 1841.

On this most memorable of all journeys of discovery nothing happened. No island was conquered, no treasure unearthed. The young doctor bled one of the twenty-eight sailors who fell ill of a fever at Surabaya. He noticed that the man's blood was bright red, as if it were coming from an artery instead of a vein. In that instant Mayer discovered the law of the conservation of energy, one of the greatest achievements of the human brain. He opened the door for the enormous technical advancement of our century.

In the isolation and unemployment of the ocean voyage Mayer had bethought himself of his books. There was the Bible, and there was a brand-new theological volume by David Frederick Strauss, who lived in Heilbronn; but what interested him most was the text-book on physiology in which the great Lavoisier advanced the doctrine that animal heat was the result of a burning process. The bright blood of the arteries was changed into the dark blood of the veins by giving off oxygen and taking up carbonic acid in the course of this process of combustion.

The brighter color of the venous blood in his sailor seemed to Mayer to prove that the loss of oxygen from arterial blood was less in the tropics than in the North because there was less heat given off from the body. But if the work done by the body is so closely related to the consumption of heat, the question arises whether the voluntary work of man, such as rubbing or hammering, may not have a fixed relation to the heat generated thereby. The helmsman one day had taught him the old Ciceronian bit of wisdom, that the storm-agitated sea is warmer than quiet sea water; also that the sea, when whipped by the wind, becomes so warm that it is easy to understand that heat must be locked up in those powerful masses of water.*

Mayer recognized with constantly increasing clearness the close connection between work and heat, their relations with each other according to some law. Lavoisier had conceived and proved in gifted fashion the conservation of matter in chemical changes, an ancient axiom of mankind, which the atomist Epicurus had already taught: "No power is able to change the sum of things. For where could even a small particle of the original matter fly to, to get out of the universe? Where could the new power be created to force its way into the All to change the whole nature of things and their movements?"

Mayer's great idea now was to extend the unchangeableness of the mass to all the processes in nature, whatever their quality might be: no cause is lost, it con-

* Cicero, *De Natura Deorum*, lib. ii, 10.

tinually passes on into an "equivalent effect," which can again serve as a new cause of a new effect. The nature of these reciprocally corresponding and interchangeable "energies" is one and the same. They can be mechanical, or they may consist of heat, light, electricity or chemical action, which up to this moment had lain near to each other without connection.

Now it came to the point where, above all, it was necessary to *measure* the amount of force if the law of the conservation of energy was to have any practical significance. One must be able to prove that when energy is transformed its relation to its measuring unit is altered, but the sum total remains the same. Mayer knew that when motion and mechanical work are stopped, they reappear in the heat produced. It was a matter, then, of finding the numerical relation between the work unit and the heat unit. This goal he later attained in the discovery of the "mechanical heat equivalent," a number on which the progress of the whole science of technical terms is based.

Mayer recognized from the first moment that his discovery was of the character of a natural law. It could be extended to all existing things in the universe, to organic and inorganic nature, to men and to the stars. *The energy of the world is constant.* "No power is able to alter its total." Physics can only recognize the forms of energy and study the conditions of its transformation.

We have experienced the marvel of this discovery repeatedly in the history of research—a discovery that suddenly broke through the blindness of generations with a power of form and content that was staggering in its completeness. Never did voice from the thornbush resound so significantly as in the thought structure which the gifted young Robert Mayer of Heilbronn erected on that little ship a-sailing the seven seas. A small-town boy from South Germany, delicate and obedient, honest and unassuming, with a well defined goal, an "anima candida," a bad pupil, a passable student, an inexperienced doctor, a beginner in everything, yet so gripped by the dæmon of his idea that it never left him again. Before his eyes looms a world of truth which he has hit upon above all other realities, and whose pains and passions will shake and torture and rejoice him to the end.

He writes to his friend, the neurologist Griesinger, on June 14, 1844:

"I hung on to the subject with such delighted interest that I—and many may laugh at me for this—asked little concerning those far parts of the earth, but preferred to remain on board where I could work without interruption, and where during many hours I felt so inspired that I can remember nothing like it before or later. Certain lightning flashes of thought that went through me—it was in the roadstead off Surabaya—

were at once eagerly followed up and led to new subjects. Those times are past, but a quiet examination of what came to the surface in me at that time has convinced me that it is a truth which is not only felt subjectively but that can be proved objectively. The day will come, that is certain, when these truths will become the common property of science."

As soon as the *Java* got back to Holland in February, 1841, with its precious freight of a new nature law, Mayer hurried back to his aging parents in Heilbronn, where he began his activities as a physician. But ceaselessly he utilized every spare moment to work out his theory, whose fundamental outlines lay clear and complete before his eyes.

On the sixteenth of June, 1841, he sent to the editors of Poggendorff's highly esteemed *Annals of Physics and Chemistry* at Leipzig a manuscript of a few pages "Concerning the Quantitative and Qualitative Determination of Forces," by J. R. Mayer, doctor of medicine and surgery, practising physician at Heilbronn. It contained, though with many an insufficient proof, the principles of the "law of the conservation of energy" in their complete significance. "Motion, heat and electricity are phenomena which can be converted into *one* force, can measure each other, and can be changed into one another under definite laws. . . .

The fundamental principle that given forces, like matter, are quantitatively unchangeable, assures us conceivably of the permanence of differences and therefore of the permanence of the material world."

This work which assured the world of the permanence of its material existence, this unique index of eternity, was found thirty-six years later, completely undamaged and unread, among the papers left at the death of Professor Poggendorff in Berlin. Mayer had never received even one word in reply, and several inquiries sent to the editor and to the publisher had brought no results.

The treatment of Mayer by the profession is all too typical of scientific history. Shortly before him (1798) Jenner had had his discovery of inoculation for smallpox returned to him by the *Philosophical Transactions* with a rude letter, and the work of Ohm—his famous law which is now the foundation of electrical science—was rejected by the Berlin philosophical faculty as "unscientific." The same sort of thing had to be endured by Ignace Philip Semmelweis, who in Mayer's day was not permitted to obviate puerperal fever by disinfecting and washing the hands. Examples may be multiplied at pleasure. Though ill-nature is by no means always the source of such hostile acts, one may well ask from what motives they do spring.

In the editorial offices of learned archives, in the uni-

versities and academies the higher administrative of-
ficials of science are in power; their department is their
world, which, besides the intellectual structure of a re-
stricted field of view contains also the social structure
of a hierarchically ordered scale of values, the lightest
disturbance of which is regarded as presumption. A
performance of genius here can often obtain proper
notice only as a work of the institution or by slipping
in as a "special contribution." Sometimes such a dagger-
thrust, exercising its revolutionary power from within
outward, so to speak, has changed the whole outline
of science. There are also privy councilors of genius
who have the luck or the cleverness to launch great
ideas authoritatively. But all too often the brilliant idea
is a new growth on the body of erudition which is felt
to be malignant and disfiguring. The pride of the experts in their little hoard of truth is deeply wounded
if an outsider comes in and tries to correct their stock
in hand. But when genius, even in its highest form,
comes forth boldly with its intellectual claims, it encounters a primitive resentment which, even in the
less vicious form of passive resistance, often brings
about the destruction of the individual, the tragic shift
of destiny for the gifted discoverer.

Mayer's simple and boyish heart succumbed to the
hardships which his exceptional position laid upon
him. The brain of a genius was housed in an average

man. Almost can one call him a lovable young buck, a genius among country folk; his thoughts shape the world picture, his days are filled with the small cares of family, food and calling. This violent contrast, this revolutionary excess of mind along with the deepest peace of soul, at first gave his spirit the right stamp.

They say that he became insane. He did indeed spend a great deal of time in asylums. He gave utterance to frightful and dangerous words of despair. His personality offers material for a clinic of manic-depressive insanity or *folie circulaire,* to use the terminology of the present day. Kretschmer, a careful and sympathetic psychiatrist, has analyzed his case quite convincingly. But Mayer was never insane if we look at him in the light of the foregoing pages. At the time when he again came in contact with the world, he was as normal as anybody else. For a man of his sort there could be nothing worse than a feeling of strangeness in a world to which otherwise he so ceaselessly belonged. For him the "law of the conservation of energy" was a definite and demonstrated fact, while for his critics it was a paranoic system, a megalomania.

One must be extraordinarily well constituted in order, as a man of normal ambitions in the course of such harsh experiences, not to be forced into the realm of the mentally ill. There he was at once received with a straitjacket and deeply embittered by barbaric senselessness. He survived this treatment. This is the surest proof of the resisting power of his spirit.

After the first attempt to inform the world of his discovery, which to his astonishment had so completely miscarried, Mayer entered into a specially fruitful correspondence with his fellow countryman, the mathematician, Karl Baur, with whom he had roomed for some time in Paris at 3 Rue de la Sorbonne. A little later he began a similar exchange of ideas with his student friend and fellow sufferer of the Questphalia Society, Wilhelm Griesinger, later famed as a Berlin psychiatrist, who at this time was a young physician in Stuttgart. In these letters of historical significance the principle of the conservation of energy took on its final and complete form.

Both of his correspondents were unbelieving at first. But it is interesting to note how much more quickly the dry and matter-of-fact Baur, whom Mayer later had to thank for personal instruction that led to a significant widening of his defective mathematical and physical knowledge, learned to understand the course of his friend's thoughts than did the more skeptical Griesinger, whose field of work was with things rather than with thoughts.

After the miscarriage with Poggendorff, and in the same year, Mayer sought out through Baur the Tübingen professor of physics, Norremberg. Here is Norremberg's verdict: "At bottom there is nothing in the way of a new view of things which one cannot view otherwise just as well. Yes, if you can base a new experiment on your theory, then, then is your case established." He asked whether Mayer could prove that fluids are heated by shaking them. Mayer went back home at once, and the experiment was a complete success.

Several weeks later he tried a similar venture with the Heidelberg physicist, Jolly. Jolly said the idea seemed good to him; Mayer should follow it up further. After this uncle-like exhortation the young man ventured, at the beginning of 1842, to hand a new sketch of his idea to Justus Liebig, at that time professor of chemistry in Giessen. The miracle happened. To Liebig belongs the undying credit of having written Mayer a friendly, approving letter. In the May issue (1842) of the *Annals of Chemistry and Pharmacy* appeared the first publication of the fundamental law: "Remarks on the Forces of Inanimate Nature." In this memorable article also is found the first calculation of the mechanical equivalent of heat, the numerical relation between heat and work: the fall of a unit of weight from a height of 365 meters is equal to the heating of a like weight of water from 0° to 1° Centigrade. (Later he corrected these figures to 425, then to 427 meter-kilograms.)

As soon as one draws the significant inference—as soon as one compares this result with the performance of our best steam engines—one sees how small a part of the heat created under the boiler is translated into motion or weight-lifting; and this can serve to justify the attempts to create motion in other ways, for instance, through the changing of chemically created electricity into useful action in the electric motor.

It is a great year in Robert Mayer's life. In August he marries the daughter of the merchant, Closs of Winnend. He is chief surgeon of the bailiwick. He plays an increasing rôle in the little city. And his book, this gigantic eruption out of the little South German city, has now come from the press.

The world allows itself to be converted to its true forward steps only reluctantly. Animals take fright suddenly and become accustomed slowly. Mischief has another, quicker dynamic than benefaction. The good deed lacks the moment of terror with which the evil deed paralyzes the understanding and enthralls the heart. Out of this difference is born the world's unrighteousness.

At the outset nothing at all happens for Mayer. After three years, in 1845, there appears in Kiel a book by Professor Christian Heinrich Pfaff—*Parallels Between the Chemical Theory and the Voltaic Contact Theory of the Galvanic Series,* etc. In this scarcely known discussion, which is as unwieldy as its title, we find the first critical estimate of the "worthy-of-all-respect essay of J. R. Mayer." For a long time this remains the only visible reaction of the world.

But the years 1842–1848 are for Mayer a period of sustained creative power. In the space of three years he brings out his *Organic Movement in Its Relation to Change of Matter* (1845), a brilliant extension of his proposition into the domain of physiology, which in part was suggested by Griesinger, and his *Contributions to the Dynamics of the Heavens* (1848), the application of the new law to the maintenance of the sun's energy. In those six years this gigantic work stands out like a towering rock in a torrent.

The complete indifference of public opinion to his trail-blazing discoveries had not yet sufficed to disturb Mayer's mental balance to any tragic extent. He was too sure of the immanent power of his truths for that. Not a trace of that later emotional damage-madness is to be seen in him, though for the most part he regarded himself as a gifted paranoic. These years of creative and unprecedentedly isolated and self-reliant labor appear to have been for him years of completely untroubled happiness in a corner. On July 11, 1843, he writes to his friend Baur:

"Things are going quite smoothly with me. My

wife's delivery of a little daughter, Wilhelmine Elise, on the 18th of May; after that the christening, plenty of official and private business, and now for weeks an important, very time-consuming project, the founding of a museum society here needed, and of which I am chief promoter, and which has called forth some rather stormy scenes in our city." *

Such were his peaceful every-day problems. But Griesinger kept urging him again and again to give a polemic and aggressive accent to his statement:

"You ought to spread some critical butter and sprinkle some polemical salt on the dry bread of mechanics and mathematics for the people. If you are convinced that the people now discussing this subject are wrong, you ought to go after them with a sharp stick and give them no rest. . . . Such attacks and peppery dishes arouse attention much more than the quiet presentation of the propositions themselves." (June 18, 1844.)

Mayer's most important book on the physiological implications of his principle, which in 1845 he again submitted to Liebig, was rejected by the publisher. A repeated discussion of the problem in the *Annals*

* Regarding the daughter here mentioned, he wrote in his *Autobiographical Note,* 1863: "When the new-born child was laid in the happy father's arms, little did he think that after twenty years this child, by translating English dramas for the father, would perform an important scientific service."

seemed to Mayer insufficient. "Inexperienced in the book business, I handed over the manuscript to the next best bookseller (Drechsler in Heilbronn), paying the printer's bill myself." Mayer showed in this essay, which has become the basis of our common physiological theories regarding food and calories, that "all mechanical operations of the animal body are performed at the cost of a slow process of combustion, and that therefore, in animals as in steam engines, the producing of motion is linked up with a consumption of heat."

This revolutionary manifesto of a new physiology, which likewise went unnoticed at first, marked the tragic turning point in Mayer's career. Besides the wounding silence of German scientists there now suddenly arose a constellation which, in the main, sought to rob him of the right to his discovery.

On August 21, 1843, James Prescott Joule of Manchester, possessor of a large brewery in Salford, presented a paper before the British Association at Cork on *The Calorific Effects of Magneto-Electricity and the Mechanical Value of Heat*. On the basis of this highly important work, whose value was recognized at once—another proof of the suggestive power of the galleries before which historical events are performed—a contest over priority sprang up between Joule and

Mayer, which was referred to the forum of the Academy of Sciences for settlement.

Shortly after his second publication Mayer had presented a memorial to the Academy (June 27, 1846) on *The Production of the Light and Heat of the Sun*. It bore the proud motto, "Simplex veri sigillum"— "Simplicity is the seal of truth." For some unexplained reason this work was not printed, nor was any report made on it. Not until the next year did the Academy, apropos of a work of Joule's, occupy itself with the subject, which now at once aroused attention. Joule's conclusions, which were a repetition of Mayer's discovery, were discussed in detail in the *Journal des Débats* (September, 1848). This caused Mayer to realise what was going on. In a letter to the Academy, presented in October, he raised the question as to the guarding of his priority. Reply and counter-reply followed. Joule, who evidently was in the wrong, would not give way, in spite of the fact that Mayer gave expression to his conviction that "Mr. Joule had made no discoveries regarding heat and energy without knowing of mine," adding: "The numerous services of this eminent physicist move me to the highest esteem. Nevertheless, I believe I am within my rights when I repeat that I was the first in 1842 to publish the law of the equivalence of heat and energy, as well as its numerical expression." (November 12, 1849.)

In this battle for his rights Robert Mayer was left
wholly without support for almost fifteen years, until
in 1862 the famous English scientist John Tyndall
took a hand in this case of human behavior and
scientific comradeship and suddenly changed the situation in Mayer's favor.

The fateful year 1848 also played a momentous rôle
in Mayer's life. Two of his children died. The political
revolt, which spread like a fever all over Europe from
the mobs of the February revolution in Paris, did not
spare even quiet Heilbronn. It led to a serious conflict
between Mayer and his radical brothers. In an attempt
to fetch back his elder brother Fritz from the rebel
volunteers he was caught and almost shot as a spy.
To be able to endure this atmosphere of grief, of sub-
terranean upheaval, of hatred and bitterness at his
own home table, required a harder training and a less
tender heart than his. He was and remained—where he
felt and did not think—a child of the romantic period,
and the vanishing of its charm gave him pain. In this
moment, when for the first time in his life the solid
walls of his ancestral house were rocking, the continuous outer confusion struck him with redoubled
force.

The article on Joule had appeared in the *Journal des
Débats*. In May, 1849, Mayer sent a short explanation of
a few lines regarding his discovery of the equivalence

of heat and work, with the title, "Important Discovery in Physics," to the Augsburg *Allgemeine Zeitung*. He was defending his priority rights against the claims of French and English scientists. In reply to this statement there appeared a few days later in the same newspaper an article by a young physicist, Otto Seyffer, in which Mayer's researches were characterized as wholly meaningless and untenable assertions and his claims to real priority of any kind denied. There followed an agitated correspondence with old Cotta, to whom the newspaper belonged, regarding this infamous act of a pompous young busybody. Mayer was not allowed to appear in print again, in spite of the fact that Seyffer a few months later, in one of his theses, published the statement: "The discovery of the so-called equivalence number between mechanical energy and heat I recognize as an established fact."

This condition of defenselessness increased Mayer's mental strain to the breaking point. A few days after receiving one of Cotta's letters—on May 28, 1850—during one of his troubled and wholly sleepless nights, when he was clad only in his nightshirt, he leaped out of his third-story window into the street. He broke both of his legs. For long weeks he lay between life and death. All the rest of his life he had a dragging gait because of the laming of his right foot. "Cause and effect are equal"—with this fundamental principle of his idea he was accustomed now and then jokingly to explain his defect.

The complete public exposure of a great despair is a serious offense against middle-class customs. Mayer's merchant father-in-law, Class, must have been horrified. His wife, that pathetic but not very superior comrade, must have trembled constantly for fear the terrible thing would happen again. Mayer was more forsaken than ever. What could have helped him—manly recognition of his achievement—was not given. He was touchingly, almost meekly thankful for every little word of encouragement. But the behavior of official science became still more cold and supercilious.

Blame for this doubtless rests with the Physics Society of Berlin, which was founded in 1845, the year when Mayer's most important book was published. Illustrious names were on its roll: du Bois-Reymond, Siemens, Traube, Helmholtz. On the program of this society was an item, "Progress in Physics," which called for regular reports on new books. The first report was dated 1845. In vain do we seek in it for the slightest mention of Mayer's *Organic Movement.* Not until 1850 is this work of genius mentioned, and then only casually and condescendingly, by Helmholtz: "The writings of Mayer and Donders are cited on account of their completeness. They contain compilations of the known facts. . . ." One can only assume, by way of excuse, that Helmholtz had not read Mayer's works at all. But in 1847 his own book, *Concerning the Conservation of Energy,* appeared. In his letter of transmission to the publisher he wrote: "The object is to give a thoroughly universal application to a fundamental principle of mechanics which has hitherto been employed only with limitations—an idea which in recent times has been agitated on many sides, but which is here for the first time completely worked out." In his book he refers to Joule and Holtzmann. Mayer is not mentioned in so much as a syllable.

The Helmholtz-Mayer case has stirred up a great deal of commotion in the scientific world. It is difficult to believe in the human fallibility of so great a man in so important a moment. But whoever studies his acts without prejudice must decide that Helmholtz behaved unfairly toward Mayer. His unlimited authority gave the death blow to Mayer's scientific reputation. In his report he refers to the priority quarrel between Mayer and Joule with the insulting and bored condescension of the university professor toward the complaining outsider. Not until Tyndall confessed before the European public the injustice that had been done to Mayer did the complainant attain his proper place. It is true that in 1877, in an ill-natured essay *On Thought in Medicine* against the existing mode of deciding priority questions only by dates without regard to the maturity of the work, Helmholtz did in unmistakable fashion indicate what ground he stood on. Above all, however, he allowed the Berlin Natural Science Society in 1866 to call him the "Father of the Law of the Conservation of Energy" without contradiction.

The chapter of the delights of intellectual possession is dark and cheerless. One might as well renounce every approximation to material satisfaction in this high sphere, and yet there is nothing more basically universal than the pride of having an idea before others. The pains endured for that idea, the formative work, the giving up to the uttermost for it, and the final achievement—these should never be stolen from a creative mind. This crime was committed against Mayer. It threw him off his mental balance. In 1851 he wrote two clear essays, admirable in diction and content—*On the Mechanical Equivalent of Heat* and *On Heart Power*.

In the same year he was sitting in the madhouse.

After a short stay in Kennenburg near Essling he passed, presumably on the advice of his wife's family, into the hands of Councilor von Zeller, who was in charge of the state insane asylum at Winnenthal. Zeller sent him on to Göppingen, into a recently established private institution under his pupil Landerer. Twenty-five years later (1877) Mayer wrote:

"I was the first to go there, and as a 'countable fool' was a welcome prey of the insanity director. I willingly pass over the details of my so-called treatment, such, for instance, as that I was tortured almost to death in the force-chair. After three months of martyrdom, on the night of July 31, 1852, tightly bound in a strait-jacket, I was dragged to Winnenthal, where, on arriving early in the morning, by order of the Councilor I was immediately strapped in a force-chair that stood ready prepared."

There is no doubt that Mayer needed temporary treatment in an asylum. His friend Rümelin describes his condition at the outbreak of his psychosis: "At home, for hours on end, half the day and all night long, he ran through every room, talking and crying out almost continuously, sometimes with words not fit to be heard, no longer keeping within his usual temperate bounds in the use of spirituous drinks, and thus worsening the situation until it was utterly unbearable for himself and his family."

Mayer had the great misfortune, as an intelligent patient, to fall into the hands of an imbecile doctor. There is no doubt that this man, who was still a devotee of the force-treatment craze of the preceding century, and into whose institution no knowledge of Pinel's beneficent reforms had penetrated, completely misunderstood Mayer's condition. This acute, purely emotional condition of manic excitement, produced by emotional causes, was mistaken by him for paranoic megalomania. In his notes Mayer writes: "I can never forget how a royal Württemberg insanity doctor in a high position passed judgment on my 'organic disturbance' in a voice of thunder: 'You have tried to square the circle!'"

The inexorableness of fate has in it something of grim comedy. Because the world does not understand him, a genius, strapped to a chair, has to listen to the weak-minded criticisms of an asylum doctor. Mayer never recovered from the wound of this psychiatric treatment. "One anxiously avoided referring to these things afterward," says a friend, "but all too often he began on them himself, and so I often heard him express himself on the subject—with great emotion, it is true, but not like one without full control of his mind and his memory. What he then uttered, as he poured forth his experiences and arguments with ever growing emotion, no one who heard him will ever be able to forget. He regarded himself as disgraced and outlawed for life."

After the family had almost forcibly compelled Mayer's release, his intellectual performances showed him to be a very clear-headed patient. Three more times—in 1856, 1865 and 1871—he returned to the Kennenburg institution, which was in the nature of a sanatorium, when he felt his acute attacks coming on. The rest of the time he followed his calling as a physician, though in reduced measure.

In 1857 a physicist named Bohn, in an article on rehabilitation, published the foolish statement that Mayer had died in the asylum shortly after the appearance of his books. Liebig made use of this information in a public lecture at Munich. Fate, which dealt out the most grotesque things to Mayer, made him feel deeply the subordinate rôle which he was playing for the world around him: almost to the day of his death he had to issue announcements and protests denying the stubborn rumor that he had died long ago. As late as 1873 the aforesaid Poggendorff, who had trifled away Mayer's first work, declared him dead beyond recall.

At the invitation of the world's fair in London in 1862, Tyndall delivered a lecture before the scientific élite of the whole world on the transformations of energy. At the close of this brilliant speech he stated that everything in it was a result of the researches of a German physician in Heilbronn whose name was almost unknown.

"When we consider the external conditions of Mayer's life and the time in which he wrote," said Tyndall, "we must be astonished at how much he achieved. This man of genius worked wholly in silence. Filled only with the love of his subject, he arrived at the most important results before all others, even though their whole lives were dedicated to scientific research."

At last Mayer was discovered. Orders and honors rained on him. The king of Württemberg gave him a title of nobility; he received the Poncelet prize and the Copley medal. The fame of Dr. Mayer of Heilbronn now waxed great also in his own fatherland. People knew who he was.

He lived to see one last dramatic triumph at the conference of physicists at Innsbruck in 1869, where he and his opponent Helmholtz held the center of the stage. Helmholtz spoke on "The Development of the New Science of Physics." Of the law of the conservation of energy he said, word for word: "In more or less common turn-about many researchers have laid this law before our eyes in the course of the last hundred years. It has been set forth in a complete generalization by Robert Mayer, who will speak later from this platform."

During the course of the address by Mayer, who at the end of a fateful career had reached the goal of being allowed to present his ideas on equal terms with Helmholtz before a historic gathering of German scientists, there arose murmurs of divers kinds. He had chosen the theme, "Necessary Consistencies and Inconsistencies of the Mechanics of Heat."

At the close of his speech there was visible unrest among his hearers. What had happened? Robert Mayer, that perpetual outsider against his will, had begun to draw the line between exact physics and metaphysics. The man who had overcome the severest shocks of his life by the power of his childlike faith had to lay it before these unbelievers:

"We step now out of the domain of inanimate nature into the living world. While there necessity rules, and the clockwork of law, we come now into a realm of purpose and beauty. . . . Figures are the boundary marks. In physics, numbers are everything; in physiology they are little; in metaphysics they are nothing." Mayer emphasized that intellectual activities are never to be identified with some kind of change going on at the same time in the brain, any more than a telegraphic dispatch is to be identified with the simultaneous electro-chemical process. It was the year 1869. Darwinism was ruling the hour. In the auditorium sat the Geneva physiologist, Carl Vogt, the stoutest advocate of scientific materialism that ever lived. His *Bigotry and Science*, Moleschott's *Circuit of Life*, Ludwig Büchner's *Power and Matter* indicate with their banality the average level of the group. Robert Mayer, daring to set God beside mathematical figures in 1869, was a heretic, just as was his Swabian fellow country-men, Kepler, who 250 years earlier had set mathemat-ical figures beside God.

Vogt wrote a hateful, garbled report for the *Köl-nische Zeitung,* with distinct allusions to Mayer's intel-lectual darkening. Mayer read it in Munich on his return trip and fell into a terrible state of mental commotion.

There followed long and quiet years of complete rest. Robert Mayer died on March 20, 1878, in his home city of Heilbronn. He remains one of the great-est of German scientists.

JACKSON AND MORTON

The Discoverers of Ether as an Anesthetic

VIII

JACKSON AND MORTON

The Discoverers of Ether as an Anesthetic

JACKSON and Morton—that sounds like the heroes of an American detective story. Jackson and Morton are the discoverers of the anesthetic quality of ether.

William Thomas Green Morton came from the little city of Charlton, Massachusetts, where he was born on August 9, 1819. When he was large enough, he was sent to Boston to learn to be a merchant, but this did not last long. At eighteen he began to study in the Baltimore Dental College. A dentist at that time was a pioneer in the forest primeval. America is the birthplace of the modern art of dentistry. It was Charles Chapin A. Harris's book, *Principles and Practise of Dental Surgery* (1839), that first laid solid foundations for this new and important branch of medical science by furnishing an exact and ingenious theory of method.

In 1841 Morton hung out his shingle as a dentist

in Farmington, then a small community in the neighborhood of Hartford, Connecticut. He was twenty-two, ambitious to make money, and determined to end his career in a larger place than Farmington. In Hartford he became acquainted with Horace Wells, a colleague four years older than he was. They both had the same object in life, so they joined hands and began dental practise together in Boston.

Wells must have been somewhat impulsive. If a thing did not succeed instantly he threw it away. The Boston enterprise did not turn out according to his wish. Before the end of the year he was back in Hartford. Morton did not go with him, but remained in Boston. There he registered as a student in Harvard College, Cambridge, and also became an assistant to a Boston physician, Dr. Charles T. Jackson.

Charles Thomas Jackson, his instructor, was fourteen years older and a rare combination of the learned and the practical. He came from Plymouth and had studied in Boston and then three years in Europe, especially in Paris. Besides his medical activities he was now pursuing chemical and geological studies on a large scale, was director of the mint, executed state commissions, made mineralogical research trips on the high seas, and opened a laboratory for chemical analyses where he also gave instruction to students. Morton lived with Jackson and was like a member of the family.

Morton fell in love with a girl and married her. Then he had to earn enough for two. His studies, scarcely begun, must again be given up. Once more he went to work as a dentist.

He had made a discovery from which he anticipated a golden future: a solder for fastening artificial teeth to gold plates. With it, fine sets of teeth could be made; but first it was indispensable that the decayed roots be removed. That meant damnable pain, and patients would rather live on gap-toothed, and do without his soldering material, than undergo such suffering. Morton found himself face to face with a dilemma: he must find a painless way to pull teeth or he would soon be looking ruin in the eye, for there was no lack of horrible dentists in Boston. He attempted it—though with only moderate results—by means of local applications of Jackson's "tooth-pain drops" consisting of a mixture of chlorin and ether.

About this time a traveling lecturer, Colton, came through Hartford and gave experimental exhibitions of the latest inventions. Among other things he demonstrated in amusing fashion the astonishing effects of so-called laughing gas.

In 1791 the freethinkers had attacked the Calvinist preacher Priestley in Birmingham, England, burned the house over his head, and destroyed his instruments. He wandered off to America and died in 1804 in Northumberland, Pennsylvania. This great discoverer of oxygen gas had also discovered nitrous oxid or laughing gas in 1776 while heating iron with nitrous acid. A little later the twenty-year-old Humphry Davy, in a so-called inhalation institute near Bristol, began working with this rare gas. As early as 1800 he wrote an essay proposing that it be used to deaden pain. But, although students at that time played all sorts of mischievous pranks with the intoxicating effects of ether in the laboratory, it occurred to no one to use these effects for any serious purpose. In 1828 an Englishman, Henry Hill Hickman, asked Charles X in Paris to have tests made as to whether laughing gas, when breathed in, had the effect of stilling pain, as certain experiments with dogs had led him to believe. The king gave the letter to the Academy and it rejected the proposition as absurd. Again in 1839 the noted surgeon Velpeau wrote: "The abolishment of pain in surgery is a chimera. It is absurd to go on seeking it today. 'Knife' and 'pain' are two words in surgery that must forever be associated in the consciousness of the patient. To this compulsory combination we shall have to adjust ourselves." That was said on the eve of a great event.

For the masses, however, the stuff bearing the sug-

gestive name of "laughing gas" was still classed with
the magnetism of Mesmer and the phrenology of Gall,
which got themselves much and secretly talked about.
Colton's demonstrations had a great vogue. In one
of these exhibitions a chemist named Cooley, be-
fuddled by the gas, fell from the chair and wounded
his knee; yet he felt not the slightest pain.

Wells was a witness of this incident. He immediately had an idea. He breathed the gas and asked
his colleague Riggs, who was in the audience, to pull
a decayed back tooth for him on the spot. The experiment succeeded beyond expectation. Wells felt
scarcely so much as a pin-prick.

Wells with his pulled back tooth and Cooley with
his skinned knee at once formed a company for painless tooth-pulling. In 1845 they appeared in Boston to
introduce themselves with a public demonstration of
this wonderful laughing gas. Morton was in the audience. The demonstration proved to be a terrible failure. The poor victims of the public execution writhed
in pain. The crowd shouted, wept and laughed. Wells
was completely discouraged. He finally gave up trying to make his fortune in the great city and went
back to Hartford, rueful and disillusioned.

Morton, however, was one of those for whom failure is a spur. There was something in this deadening

effect of gas. It must be investigated. Risks must be taken. One must not give up. His colleague Wells had been daunted by the cries of his poor victims. But not he! He had ascertained that the freedom from pain was not complete, that it lasted only a short time. The failure was half a success.

Morton thought again of Jackson's ether drops, which killed the pain of sick nerves for a short time. A treatise written by Faraday in 1818 fell into his hands, and in it the pain-deadening effects of laughing gas were compared with those of sulfuric ether. He procured a large flask of sulfuric ether, some fish, chickens, dogs and whatever he could lay his hands on, and let the ether reach the animals. One day a dog refused to endure such treatment, knocked over the table, and acted like a mad dog. The expensive ether flask lay broken on the ground. Morton knelt down and wiped up the liquid with a cloth, then sniffed the cloth. A little later his mother, to her consternation, found him lying senseless and snoring on the ground. The first anesthesia had succeeded.

Morton guarded his precious secret carefully. He saw in imagination the teeth of all Boston in his dentistry chair. Tirelessly he went on trying out sulfuric ether upon his animals, yet without definite results. He was dissatisfied and perplexed. His animals became excited, restless, cross and inclined to bite, but they did not sleep. There must be something wrong with his technique. Perhaps there is too much air mixed with the gas, perhaps the gas flows too fast.

At last Morton goes to his teacher, Jackson, and asks for the loan of an airtight tube. What does he want it for? He has an anxious patient, a nervous lady who faints at the slightest pain; he will use the tube to blow air into her mouth, at the same time telling her that it is a magic means of banishing pain —a sort of technical mesmerism.

Jackson is a man of strong principles and professional honor. He does not like suggestive short-cuts of this sort, and advises his pupil to experiment with sulfuric ether. However, he is not to use the commercial ether mixed with alcohol, but a pure, rectified ether that can be obtained from the Burton laboratory. Morton, who knows what he is about, acts as if he has never heard the words sulfuric ether. The secret must not yet pass his lips.

Morton obtains from Burton a suitable amount of pure sulfuric ether. Then he seats himself at home in a comfortable armchair, takes his watch in his hand, pours the ether on his handkerchief and lays it over his mouth and nose. When he comes to himself again, exactly eight minutes have passed. In that time one could easily pull three teeth.

In the evening of the same day fate rings at Morton's door in the form of the musician Frost. The date is September 30, 1846. Frost is gigantic and powerful, but he is trembling with pain in a back tooth. He wants to have it out, but he has heard of the wonders of mesmerism and wishes to be magnetized first. Morton says mesmerism is out of date, but he has something much better, a gas that has to be breathed in. Frost consents gladly, and breathes under the cloth. After five minutes he is rid of his tooth without knowing it happened.

Morton feels now that his hour has come. He immediately makes a formal record of the facts, and Frost, Morton and a Dr. Hayden who had assisted, sign it. The next morning the excited citizens of Boston read in the *Daily Journal*:

October 1—Last evening a man had a tooth pulled without experiencing any pain. He was thrown into a kind of sleep by inhaling a preparation whose effect lasted about a minute, just long enough to pull the tooth.

Morton had succeeded. The thing began to be the talk of the town. The cautious Jackson warned his pupil to guard against disappointments and made a good suggestion. It was now essential, he said, to test the new treatment more thoroughly in the presence of a professional audience at the General Hospital.

Accordingly Morton went to the head surgeon, Dr.

J. Warren, who was regarded as the leading surgeon of New England. Warren came of one of the oldest families in the country, one of the old Revolutionary families whose name every schoolboy knows. Dr. Warren deserves honorable mention in history because he, famous authority as he was, gave an unknown young dentist a chance without many formalities.

Within a few days Morton received an invitation from the second surgeon, Dr. Hayward, to appear in the Massachusetts General Hospital on Friday, October 16, at 10 o'clock in the morning. A patient had to undergo an operation, and Morton was to use upon him the new means he had discovered for making one insensible to pain. In all haste he contrived an inhalator, a glass globe to contain the ether-saturated sponge, which protruded on two sides in a cylindrical extension. One opening was closed with a cork, on the other a hose was attached for inhaling. In this tube, in front of the glass cylinder, was a valve-like ball that worked like a self-opening and self-closing membrane when the patient breathed in and out.

Shortly before 10 o'clock on that sixteenth of October Morton is running back and forth in the workshop of Chamberlain, the instrument maker, roaring like a lion. He is waiting for his apparatus, which has not been finished in time.

Meanwhile, in the amphitheater of the hospital, whose classic cupola and columned façade dominate the houses for blocks around, seven physicians in their official frock coats have already assembled. Round about on the benches the students crowd in. Old Warren, from minute to minute, looks impatiently at his watch. In the background the great washbowls stand ready. The patient lies in trousers and shirt, with bared neck, on the white cover of the operating table. He is the twenty-year-old book printer, Gilbert Abbott, who wishes to be rid of a swelling that has troubled him since birth on the right side of his jaw.

The clock hands move on. No Morton appears. Finally Warren takes his knife in hand and remarks amid the ironic laughter of the spectators: "Since Mr. Morton has not come, I presume he is busy elsewhere."

At the dramatic moment when Warren is applying the knife to the skin of the patient, in comes the overheated Morton with his glass globe. He is accompanied by his witness, the musician, Frost.

Morton pours the ether, whose smell he has disguised by reducing it to a liquid with a pleasant odor, upon the sponge. "Are you afraid?" he asks Abbott, that historic model of the courageous patient. Abbott answers no, and takes the breathing tube in his mouth. The procedure begins.

Curiously and with ill-controlled uneasiness every-body stares at young Abbott's head. The lips under Morton's mustache, which looks a good deal like a Newfoundlander's, are pressed tightly together. The patient begins to groan, turn restlessly from side to side, and babble nonsense. A cloud of doubt gathers ominously. The movements become more violent, the voice grows thick, the clenched fists drop open. Suddenly Abbott is asleep. His restful and regular breathing can be heard plainly in the room, which has become altogether silent. Not the slightest sound disturbs the deep, almost magical silence.

The knife cuts the skin over the swelling, cuts the tissue under the skin, cleaves the muscle, and, plunging deep, lifts out the tumor. After some five minutes the lips of the patient begin to move, he stammers a few incomprehensible words that might be regarded as cries of pain. The operation is over. The wound is covered with a compress. Abbott regains consciousness. He declares that he felt nothing but a little light scraping with a dull knife.

"Indeed, indeed, gentlemen, this is no humbug," cries Warren, the sober, correct Warren, stirred to enthusiasm. Thunderous applause goes through the hall. At the door the surgeon, Dr. H. Bigelow, who had opposed the operation, was heard to say to an acquaintance: "I have seen something today that will be heard of around the world."

Cautiously one doctor after another ventures into the unknown land of painlessness. The next day Hayward operates, with Morton's assistance, on a woman with a large fatty growth on the right shoulder. The same day Dr. Dix undertakes the removal of a surface growth on the face, which keeps the patient under the anesthetic more than thirty minutes. This operation almost had a fatal ending: the patient's face went blue and the breath stopped. Fortunately, Bigelow, who was again present, took a hand in it. He was the first to recognize that the stopping of the pulse marks the extreme limit for the duration of a narcosis.

A larger operation, one that was destined to have a decisive influence on the further use of inhalation anesthesia, was scheduled for the seventh of November. The patient was Alice Mohaw, a girl of twenty years who was suffering from tuberculous suppuration of the knee joint, which compelled the doctors to amputate the leg. Shortly before the appointed time, Hayward, second in command of the hospital staff, refused his consent to the use of anesthetics. The first opposition was beginning to make itself felt. Morton was blamed for keeping the secret of his discovery and not making known the composition of his gas.

Morton promised to give Warren a written description of his discovery on condition that his secret should be kept during the interval when he was applying for a patent. But this not altogether unequivocal concession did not satisfy the doctors. A resolution was passed, under which it was agreed that they would keep away from Morton because of his secrecy, and would forego the use of anesthesia.

Bigelow, who is one of the few in the history of ether narcosis who played a thoroughly unselfish and humanly magnificent rôle, intervened. The day for the operation had come. Bigelow got hold of Morton and took him into the hospital, where he hid him in a back room. Then he began making serious remonstrances to the doctors. This was a question, not of medical etiquette, he said, but of humanity. Moreover, Morton had formally stated in a letter to Warren that he had used sulfurous ether for his treatment. This information appeased the doctors. Warren pulled Morton's letter out of his pocket and made known the gist of its contents. The staff now decided to give its permission, since Morton had fulfilled the conditions laid down to him.

Morton was brought out of his hiding place, and head after head appeared in the room—physicians, jurists, clergymen, students—all desiring to witness the great decisive battle against pain.

Hayward steps to the operating table and offers a short explanation. He says that, with the consent of his colleagues, he is about to let his patient breathe a vapor which is said to have the power to banish the pain of the operation.

Morton begins his work. In order to get through quickly, Hayward begins cutting with great slashes. The knife goes through the thigh and prepares the upper flap. The patient lies in deep, restful sleep. The second flap is cut. The bone is sawed through. Five arteries are bound up tightly. With the sixth and last artery the woman begins to groan. It is the first sign of feeling, but the amputation is already finished. The patient wakes after a few minutes and looks around astonished. She knows nothing of an operation and will not believe that her leg has just been taken off.

Deep emotion and endless rejoicing sweep over those present. They all feel that it is a great moment in human history. The Medusa's head of anguish, the writhings of pain, the threat of physical torture appear to be things of the past. The dentist Morton has achieved something more than the painless installing of artificial teeth; he has freed the physician from the fearful fetter of human cries and exalted the curative art into the realm of the wonderful and incomprehensible.

The story of surgery is a terrible story of suffering. Since the beginning of recorded time, all that men had ever thought of for combating this suffering was in vain. From the opium of the Chinese, the mandragora of Dioscorides, the "sleep sponges" of the Middle Ages that made one "foolish and absurd" (H. von Gersdorff), to the deep intoxication of alcohol; from the pressing together and binding up of the blood vessels and nerves, the ice-colds and glowing-hots, to the letting of blood until one became unconscious, every attempt brought only failure and disappointment. It is one of the great miracles of human endurance and superiority that surgery, in this hand-to-hand battle with death, again and again struck down these fearful weapons of pain and infection—by the improvement of medical methods—even when it was still powerless to banish them.

The use of the new method spread over the globe with amazing speed. As early as December, 1846, the first narcoses were carried into effect in London and Paris. The first German anesthesia was employed successfully on January 24, 1847, by Hayfelder in Erlangen. In a few months the treatment was the common property of the profession.

But now there develops among the originators of this great achievement a battle of truly Balzacian hatred and infamy. An evil destiny drives these bold and gifted spirits into a morass of baseness in which each sinks from sight in his own particular way. It is difficult to get a clear understanding of the cause—ambition or greed or envy—which brought this curse upon the good deed. Naturally there was no lack of countercharges in the affair, but they were soon doomed to silence by their complete want of substance. Thus at the beginning of 1847 the editor of the Philadelphia *Medical Examiner* writes: "We would not regard the scandal as worth mentioning if the Boston *Medical Journal* did not inform us that eminent members of the medical profession have let themselves get caught in this net." And the New York *Journal:* "This latest marvel has already found its natural end, and has sunk in the great abyss that has swallowed up so many of its predecessors."

Much worse, however, was the damage which Morton's morbid business ethics did to his own cause. As early as November, 1846, wretched patent litigation was in full swing. In the preceding month Morton's attorney, Eddy, had applied for a patent. Eddy recommended the inclusion of Jackson in this patent with a share of 10 per cent of the profits; but Jackson refused to go into it because he would run the risk of being barred from the medical fraternity of Massachusetts by the stiff wording of the statute. He wanted $500 "for advice given," and then Morton could do what he wished with the patent. Finally, through a mediator, Dr. Gould, an agreement was reached on this basis, and Jackson renounced all right and title to the authorship of the discovery.

Meanwhile Bigelow appeared before the Academy of Arts and Sciences in Boston and made the first public report, November 13, 1846, of an amputation completed under an anesthetic; and this set out on its journey through the world.

The sensation of the whole affair, the volcanic outpouring of fame and honor, of praises and rewards, which was waiting to drop on the head of the discoverer, vitiated the judgment and normal faculties of all parties concerned.

Jackson, who hitherto had scarcely concerned himself with his share of the credit, and who seemed quite satisfied with his $500, suddenly came forward with loud assertions of his sole claim to the discovery. On March 2, 1847, he gave a lecture before the Boston Academy in which he made no mention of Morton and acted as if all the experiments in the hospital were conducted and initiated by himself. A day or two later this lecture was published in the *Advertiser* and was forthwith dispatched to Europe on the next mail steamer. With time the quarrel grew to ever more threatening proportions.

In a letter intended for the French Academy and addressed to Dr. de Beaumont, an acquaintance of Jackson in his Paris days, Jackson designated himself as the sole discoverer of ether narcosis. Paris was somewhat perplexed over the different accounts of the Boston proceedings. Velpeau, in a session of the Academy, defended the view that the secret revealed in Jackson's letter had long been no secret at all, since American professional journals had announced the new discovery weeks ago.

Bigelow, immediately after the amputation, had written to Dr. Boot in London describing it in detail. On December 21, 1846, the British surgeon Liston performed an upper-thigh operation with anesthetics. Liston cried in enthusiasm: "Hurrah! Glorious! An American dentist has given us ether to banish pain. In six months there will be no operations without ether!"

In the following year the physicians of the Massachusetts Hospital drew up a memorial to the Congress of the United States proposing that a suitable national reward be given to the discoverer of ether narcosis— after the various claims had been weighed. In return for this, all patent rights were to be renounced in the public interest. Morton agreed. Jackson opposed. He would recognize no tribunal on the subject and desired as his reward only the thanks of mankind.

Congress has never decided the matter. All attempts of Morton, who fell into ever deeper poverty, to obtain from Washington any material recognition of his service were thwarted by the bitter opposition of Jackson's partizans, continued through the years. Morton never had any use of his patent. It seems to be one of those rare cases in which the rights of society over a good thing so necessary to life were maintained regardless of a documented legal claim. In the war which the United States waged in 1848 against Mexico for possession of Texas and California, ether anesthesia was generally used, and it was adopted without further ado by clinics everywhere. The patent, that object of unholy strife, was entirely worthless.

Wells, too, suddenly came forward with discovery claims, although only two months earlier he had heartily wished success to Morton in Hartford. The feeling that he had come so close to a great event gave him no rest. He designated himself—in a Hartford newspaper—as the first real discoverer of anesthesia. When nobody would believe him, he swallowed chloroform in January, 1848, in New York, and departed this life.

The only one who kept his head was Bigelow, who from the first moment had taken his stand, with all his authority, for Morton: "Morton desired my presence and my advice as a physician, but the anesthesia belongs to him. I took no responsibility upon myself. Had the first patient died in the stupor, as could easily have happened, Morton is the one who would have been responsible. Since the patient did not die, the glory belongs to him."

Through the rest of their lives Jackson and Morton were poor, sad pensioners of fame. They gathered orders and diplomas, but always with a secret view to making them count in the battle against each other. The brilliant discovery which bound their names forever to each other became for them a torturing fetter of hate. According to a barbaric custom of the East, a debtor was chained to his creditor and had to accompany him continually; so here both together were regarded as the creditor. When Jackson, through Humboldt's intervention, was made a knight of the Red Eagle by the king of Prussia, the czar of Russia chose to honor Morton; Italy and Turkey voted for Jackson, Sweden for Morton. It was a wrangling, tragicomic tug-of-war, with honors serving for the rope. The Monthyon prize of the French Academy for "benefactors of mankind" was divided: Jackson received 2500 francs "for his observations and experiments in regard to the anesthetic effects of breathing

ether," and Morton got 2500 francs "for the introduction of this method into surgical practise." Morton
received an honorary doctorate from Harvard, and
finally the authorities of the Massachusetts Hospital
handed him a silver bowl filled with a thousand dollars. But by that time he was a completely ruined man,
fallen into poverty. The report of the hospital counselor
said: "He is impoverished by a thing which has made
the world his debtor."

Jackson lived with his hatred to the age of seventy-
five. On the perilous brink of insanity and monomania
he pursued the way of his unhappiness with blind
certainty to the end. He died in 1880 in the neighborhood of Boston.

Morton was felled by an apoplectic stroke in 1868,
in Central Park, New York, immediately after reading
a new hate-writing of Jackson against himself. At
Mount Auburn near Boston stands his tombstone:

W. T. G. Morton
The Inventor and Discoverer
of Anesthesia
Before him, Surgery Meant Agony
Through him the Tortures of the Knife
Were Averted and Annihilated
Since Him, Science is Master over Pain
Erected by the Citizens of Boston

So ends the sad story of Jackson and Morton and
their liberating achievement. They were scientific

prodigies, they had the gifts of medical talent, technical skill, and early maturity in their profession. They let themselves be lured by the spotlight of publicity. The multitude yearns for the proud, beaming face of its hero; but the benefactor of mankind in this case was a poor, vain, earthly dentist. He was betrayed by the illusion of "the great man" and had to atone for it. Like a film star who no longer draws, he was forgotten. But his great venture against pain will remain deathless.

The conquest of pain has not stood still. As a tamed element it is allowed to fulfil its moral mission, but it can no longer perpetrate its former devastations. A year after the discovery of ether anesthesia, the English accoucheur, James Young Simpson, introduced chloroform. Other chemical combinations followed. After a few years (1853) came the discovery of how to inject anesthetics under the skin—through the Edinburgh physician, Alexander Wood, and the Frenchman, Charles Gabriel Pravaz. This technical advance made possible one of the most fruitful methods of modern medicine. Through it the rational use of alkaloids and other narcotic substances first became possible for the physician. Morphin, discovered in 1805 by the Gladbeck druggist Sertürner, now began its triumphant march. In 1859 cocain was produced in Wöhler's

laboratory, and in 1884 it was introduced into medicine by Carl Koller as one of the most effective
anesthetics for the mucous membrane.

In 1891 Carl Ludwig Schleich was denied a chance
to speak before the Berlin Surgical Society, under Bar-
deleben's presidency, when he wished to hand over
to the scientific world the principles of local anesthesia,
which he had discovered through the infiltration
method that he had been employing. Anesthesia of
the spinal marrow was introduced into surgery by
Bier. Only in recent years has the deadening of pain
by the injection of narcotic matter into the veins
further humanized the methods of anesthesia and reduced the danger that can arise through irritation of
the lung tissues.

The civilization of pain has arrived. The amount of
pain has not been lessened; the sum total is rather
greater. But since the mechanics of the origin and the
avoiding of pain have been so thoroughly investigated,
the fear has become less and the readiness to endure
has become greater. The animal cry had grown to be
a human hardship, a dreaded specter. Pain, that great
and helpful comrade of life, that surest proof of existence, is man's eternal witness against death.

MAX JOSEPH VON PETTENKOFER

Founder of Modern Hygiene

IX

MAX JOSEPH VON PETTENKOFER

Founder of Modern Hygiene

"If the human race can be perfected, it is in
medicine that we must look for the means."
—Descartes.

PETTENKOFER is the man who swallowed the
cholera bacilli. But it is not only this rare and
moving act in defiance of the sober arguments of science
that distinguishes him. Pettenkofer, who lived from
1818 to 1901, both woke up and went into the night
with his century. This bold and thoughtful man, with
his shock of white hair, his gentle air and his look of
wise superiority, this head of a modern Æsculapius,
at the beginning of the new century carefully and
determinedly ended his fully rounded life with a shot
in the head.

His work, manifold and apparently based upon an
unplanned but ceaseless observation and thinking-
through of phenomena, almost recalls the encyclopedias of the Renaissance in its wide and comprehen-

255

sive universality. But at that time man had first to seek his place in the universe and confine the shadow of his soul in the newly discovered house of flesh and blood, which, like the star and the dust, was ruled by the newly discovered laws of nature. Pettenkofer's whole work finally flowed out into a magnificent view of the physiology of the human world.

He founded the scientific hygiene of our time, the attempt to know and control everything that through external influence can hinder or promote the life and activities of man. From the sewer to the soul, from climate to drainage this medical sociology throws light upon the laws of human well-being and reaches down deeply and decisively into the organism of our economic and political relations. The question of individual and social ability to do things is the question of the fate of mankind, and it is primarily a medical question, not national-economic, not political, not technical; and so far, at least, as man has a hand in shaping his own fate, it can be solved by physicians and only by them.

Pettenkofer's scientific career was a product of that great and tragic nineteenth century, which broke down under its wealth of discoveries and civilizing deeds like a tree under the excess of its fruit. The avalanche of ever-swelling change in the conditions of human life, through the growth of cities, the increase of indi-

vidualism, the speeding up of intercourse, the increase
of necessities, the growth of population, the reshaping
of social classes—all these produced a vast amount of
shaking up and general disturbance. Pettenkofer was
one of the first to regard the fateful changes of
humanity as the sufferings of a single gigantic animal
organism, and to ascribe the form and progress of
epidemics and illnesses not to the hardships and ills
of single individuals but to mass movements, mass
causes, mass conditions. Thereby, as the conclusion
of four centuries of development, he brought the
knowledge of the body and its functions, the place
of man in nature, into the new coherence of a practical
biology rich in promise for the future.

Modern hygiene is an experiment suited to our time,
a universal quest to be pursued with the compass of
a great central idea; for there is scarcely a department
of natural science that does not have to play a part
in the solution of questions of hygiene.

When Pettenkofer was born on December 13, 1818,
in Lichtenheim, a lonely and remote village on the
upper Danube near Neuburg, the first cries of alarm
were rising over the fearful cholera epidemic, which
for the first time had that year crossed the boundaries
of India and reached the edges of Europe. Like a
leitmotif this cry of terror went with him through
life. As an eighteen-year-old pupil he held in his arms

a friend laid low by the scourge. When in 1854 this
illness, then on its third conquering invasion, broke
out in Munich with devastating power and seized victims even in his own family, he plunged into the researches on cholera which thenceforth to the end of
his life consumed a large part of his working strength.

The father, who continued to farm the estate of his
ancestors, a former toll station between the electorate
of Bavaria and the dukedom of Neuburg, had a hard
fight to make ends meet with his eight children. It
was fortunate for the family that the father's older,
childless brother, Dr. Franz Xaver Pettenkofer, surgeon and apothecary to the Bavarian court, took four
of the farmer's children, one after another, to live
with him in the city. At the age of eight Max Pettenkofer was living in his uncle's official residence in
Munich, which thenceforth became his second home.

He was a brilliant student in the gymnasium and
desired to specialize in the philology of the classic
tongues. His uncle, however, had secret hopes of making him his successor as court apothecary; so he had
him study the natural sciences and pharmacy, and after
two more years (1833) made him an apprentice in the
dispensary, where, after another year, he promoted him
to the position of assistant with an allowance of a
florin a day.

The uncle was affectionate, but Bavarian. When

Pettenkofer one day made a slight mistake in the shop, he received a frightful thrashing. The same day he was up and off. To the consternation of his family, the twenty-year-old came to the surface later in the city theater at Augsburg, where, with his long name cut off before and behind, as Tenkof he was playing the part of Brackenburg in *Egmont* and of Astolf in Calderon's *Life a Dream*.

The Augsburg press is not enthusiastic in its criticisms, but no prayers or exhortations can get Pettenkofer away from his new calling. Only when his cousin Helen, daughter of an officer of the exchequer in Augsburg from the little city of Friedberg, beseeches him "to be again a regular man and return to his studies" and promises then to be his forever, does the sinner surrender. The family breathes again, not having to count a comedian among its members. The uncle is appeased, but he insists now that Pettenkofer shall study medicine, not chemistry, as he had before. For the court apothecary a former show-actor is a creature forever lost. "Such a man is fit at best to be a medical doctor."

From the beginning of his study Pettenkofer developed an extraordinary activity. Apparently without effort he would reach up and pick a formless problem out of the air like a magician, and every time it would change in his hand into something with form and meaning. When he was seeking his doctor's degree in 1842 he had already discovered a sure and simple method of proving the presence of arsenic in a murder trial; also a perfect method of distinguishing arsenic from antimony, which has remained unsurpassed to this day. In 1843 he took a whole bunch of examinations: the license as apothecary, the state examination as physician, and the collegiate doctorate, which he won with a noteworthy thesis on a tropical plant, Micania Guaco, with the extract of which he had experimented upon himself.

Pettenkofer had steadily shown a considerable aversion to medical practise. The reason is perhaps evident when one recalls the fact that German medicine at the time of his first impressions was still predominantly under the influence of the nature-philosophy of Schelling's school, whose tendency toward sheer speculation would naturally arouse the strongest opposition in a young fellow interested in chemical experiments. Whoever wished to heal, in those days, must first philosophize. His great longing was to go to Liebig in Giessen, whose famous school was the Mecca of students interested in chemistry. As there was no immediate opening there, however, he went with a scholarship for organic chemistry to Liebig's pupil, Scherer, at Würzburg.

Here again he had soon done some important things.

In a child kept on a wholly vegetarian diet he found a considerable amount of hippuric acid, which had hitherto been found only in plant-eating animals. On this he based a convincing demonstration of the influence of diet upon the composition of the kidney secretions. Then followed the Pettenkofer reaction for the detection of gall acids, still known by his name today. The most important work of this chemical-physiological period has to do with the discovery of creatin in the urine, which he began in Würzburg and finished in 1844 with Liebig, to whom he finally obtained access. For Liebig this find was of supreme value, since for the first time it assured an exact insight into the changes that occur in meat when it is taken as food and gave him the basis for his *Chemical Researches on Meat,* published in 1847.

In the autumn of 1844 Pettenkofer returned to Munich, but he found it impossible, although he already had a good name as a chemist, to obtain a position or any chance to work. An offer of a university position as physiological-chemical researcher was held up by lack of the final order, and remained suspended there. The young scientist lay fallow and suffered for bread.

In this situation he accepted the post of assistant in the office of the mint at Munich. Now he was earning a florin and a half a day, had the prospect of an orderly official life, and could at last marry Helen, the guardian angel who had rescued him from the comedian's hell.

At first the doctor in the position of mint assistant was regarded as a grotesque misfit. But soon people discovered with astonishment the extraordinary character of the new official. All the Brabant dollars were at once called in and reminted in accordance with the German standard. He succeeded in doing what all the mint employees had hitherto been unable to accomplish: he determined the silver content of the silver coinage and simplified and reduced the cost of refining gold and silver. These practical results won the greatest respect from the realists of the mint. They no longer wondered that the famous Professor Wöhler, discoverer of synthetic urea, paid a visit to the mint, not to see the director, but to make the acquaintance of the youngest assistant, Pettenkofer.

The chemical laboratory of the mint inspired Pettenkofer to still other experiments. In saliva he discovered the poisonous sulfocyanic acid. Another chemical quest, however, was destined to give a decisive turn to his career.

The art-loving King Ludwig I had sent a commission of savants and artists to Pompeii to study the forgotten technique of ancient art handiwork. From this trip they had brought back a piece of wonderful opaque glass, blood-red in color, the so-called por-

porino antico, which Pliny had described in his natural history as bloodstone. The art of making this glass was wholly lost, and the Munich professors were unable to fulfil the king's desire for red glass to use in his buildings. Pettenkofer solved this chemical problem for him, and later, after the king's resignation in favor of Maximilian II, he practically perfected the technique for the making of colored art glass.

For Pettenkofer the rediscovery of the ancient purple had an immediate result: the enthusiastic king in 1847 gave him the university chair of medical chemistry—after the proposition had reappeared out of the dust of conflict attending the fall of Abel's ministry. With a yearly income of seven hundred florins, two bushels of wheat and seven bushels of corn he began his academic career.

It was hard to make a gifted scholar out of this gifted hand worker. Every practical difficulty fascinated him; he had an infallible instinct for technical problems. In 1849 the architect Leo von Klense brought him samples of English Portland cement which were far superior to the hydraulic plaster made in Germany. This was the right kind of task for Pettenkofer. In a short time he produced definite specifications as to the time of burning and the proper degree of heat for the different kinds of marl in order to guarantee a

German product just as good as the much more expensive Portland cement.

Gaslight had been streaming over the streets of London since 1814, for Murdock had published his sensational discovery of gas lighting in 1803. Gas lighting became the ambition of every city government. The enormous price of coal, however, presented a serious obstacle to this technical advance in South Germany. Pettenkofer attempted to make lighting gas out of the "pitch wood" that was so cheap around his old home. By increasing the heat he succeeded in improving the lighting power of the wood gas. The process was adopted by the city of Basel. The formal opening of the gas works attracted spectators from all over Europe. The hour for lighting up had come. Pettenkofer was there. But when the illumination should have blazed forth there was only a weak, flickering, wretched light. The new factory would have to be scrapped!

Pettenkofer went back to Munich with tears of rage and humiliation running down his cheeks, rushed from the railway station to his laboratory, and in two days of intensive work corrected the error by a change in the opening from which the gas issued. Soon bright jets of wood gas were lighting the chief railway station of Munich, and the process had its industrial value until a change in the price of tubing made it impractical.

An especially valuable achievement, though entirely outside of his domain, was his discovery of a process for renovating old paintings. An art historian, Pecht, called attention in 1851 to the sad condition of the restored pictures in the Munich galleries. A commission was appointed, to which Pettenkofer belonged, and he succeeded in finding out the chemical cause of the mold-like dimming of the varnish. By blowing off with alcohol and air in the case of resin varnishes, or by rubbing with a soap made of copaiba balsam and ammonia in the case of oil varnishes, Pettenkofer was able to restore the pictures completely. This process, still generally used today, was later purchased by the Bavarian Government.

A highly significant chemical discovery was made public by Pettenkofer in 1850 at a session of the Munich Academy where he revealed his discovery of the regular intervals between the atomic weights of the elements. Because of lack of funds he could not go on with these fundamentally important calculations, which were later widened by Mendeleyeff. His figures remained almost unknown and were rediscovered eight years later by the French chemist Dumas; then people recalled Pettenkofer's priority. Fifty years later the German Chemical Society, in honor of this foundation work on atomic weights, had a medal struck off for Pettenkofer, then an old man. He was, as this discovery proves, also a theorist of a high order.

But for Pettenkofer, who, though a physician, almost anxiously avoided the uncertain ground of the healing art, all these happy solutions of hard problems were only the introduction to the project of his great social science of hygiene. After he had had his fill of such problems—in the difficult year 1848, at the age of twenty-nine—he delivered an academic address, *Chemistry in Its Relation to Physiology and Pathology,* in which he said:

"A man of pure science always concerns himself first with truth; but who is so through-and-through a philosopher that he is not, as a citizen of his country, as head or member of a family, forced to ask himself: 'What is left from my experiences and from the results of my thinking that will serve to rejoice the hearts and lighten the sufferings of those with whom we are together so short a time here on earth?' As a man the savant is bound to think of this, and he is either a weakling or a monster if he thinks or acts otherwise."

Without this moral impulse toward the shaping of a better world, without this social idea in his work, Pettenkofer would have remained all his life merely an inventor with a lucky knack.

The change from gifted inventor to gifted researcher

lies immediately ahead. After the death of his uncle in 1850 he was called by King Maximilian II to succeed him as court apothecary and took possession of the official residence in the capital where his youth had been passed. Here an incident changed him from a technician into a hygienist. The Meissen air-heating system had been introduced into the court. But the king disliked the feel of the dry heat in his castle and commissioned his medical staff to investigate the question whether hot air was injurious to health. Pettenkofer was asked for his opinion.

Out of this grew the beginning of a new science. With a thoroughgoing and systematic investigation of the air in the royal Bavarian court Pettenkofer shaped the foundations of experimental hygiene. He advanced into the halls like the leader of a meteorological expedition. To the astonishment of everybody he established the fact that the air was not drier but moister than with stove heating, because of the absorption of water out of the walls by the heat conduits. The feeling of dryness was due to the five times greater circulation of air which the new heating system produced. Thus he discovered the true cause of the dampness of new dwellings and the reason for their penetrating coldness—the constant air-stream through the pores of the wet stone walls.

With this investigation there begins for Pettenkofer

an endless series of problems of a new kind; but now he has found the central point for his researches—the world of men. Through his studies of ventilation in dwellings he comes to the question of the hygienic function of the house in which we pass our days and which he regards as "a bell dropped over a bit of earth." From the wide garment of the home a self-evident step leads to the investigation of the physiological value of our clothing, to which he devoted his attention in 1857 and 1865 in comprehensive treatises. What he dealt with here—the regulation of the outflow of heat, the hygroscopic characteristics of clothing materials, their airtightness, the cooling effect of linen, the amount of evaporation through the skin, and countless other questions—all this was entirely new ground. "In our clothes we find ourselves as if naked in a windless atmosphere of 75 to 86 degrees Fahrenheit." The bald realism of such scientific statements sounded almost comic in the ears of hearers accustomed only to theories, but their practical usefulness killed every smile of mockery in the bud.

Pettenkofer's new studies had to do not with the last and greatest things, but with the smallest, humblest, most everyday phenomena of our well-being and discomfort; yet through his wholly unmetaphysical explanations we sense the presence of a wonderful and intelligent mechanism in the realm of our commonest habits and bodily functions.

The course of his researches and the way he circled around a central idea in handling his materials can be traced with almost barometric certainty in the titles of his lectures. At first he dealt with *Organic Chemistry in its Application to Physiology and Pathology;* the same theme bobbed up in 1853: *Lectures on Dietetic Physical Chemistry.* Here he is already teaching the composition of air, water, meat, milk, bread. Then come *Concerning the Physical and Chemical Principles of Dietetics and the Care of the Public Health, Medical Policing with Regard to the Physical and Chemical Principles of Health Science, Public Health Duties of Physicians, Architects, Engineers, Etc.,* until finally all writings on his new scientific ideas cease. In the summer of 1865 he called his addresses for the first time *Lectures on Hygiene.*

Pettenkofer, of course, did not found hygiene. It is an elementary concern of mankind, the key to the survival of every powerful social and political system, and the ultimate life wisdom of every true health staff. But he did raise hygiene to the rank of a modern science and make it, instead of a negligible addendum to medical instruction, the chief branch in the study of medicine.

"I conceive of hygiene as the housekeeping economy

of health, just as national economics deals with the economy of goods. As in national economics the motive power is not so much the fear of loss, but much more the striving for higher gains, so must it be also in hygiene as health economy. Hygiene has the mission of investigating and controlling all the natural and artificial surroundings of the organism, in order, through knowledge of them, to promote its welfare."

The ground on which he began his work was auspiciously prepared beforehand. In 1779 the first volume of Johann Peter Frank's *Medical Police* had appeared and had for the first time in Germany placed the question of public health on a broad basis of statewide importance. Jenner's brilliant discovery of smallpox inoculation in 1796 gave a convincing example of the beneficence of a forward-looking attention to illness. Benjamin Thompson, later Count Rumford, when he was a citizen of Munich by choice, had for the first time acted on the idea that caring for the poor was a duty of humane reason, a necessary contribution to the solving of social crises and not merely a work of mercy. He gave work to the poor, gave them sleep, clothing, food, a clean place to live in, and even his bitterly criticized "Rumford soup" made of bone gelatin—that rationalized poor soup— was justified later by food physiology.

Statistics are a product of the seventeenth century.

In 1662 an Englishman, Captain John Graunt, began the use of "political arithmetic," and was the first to compute social mass phenomena by definite laws. But only when Euler, Laplace, Fournier had formulated the underlying principles of probability and Bernoulli had discovered the "law of large numbers" was Quételet able in 1835 to define the laws governing the phenomena in the lives of men by exact mathematical methods and thereby make statistics one of the most important scientific aids for hygiene. Besides the important data on movements of the population, illnesses, births, causes of death, it was possible, above all, with the help of statistics, to figure out the financial significance of an illness in loss of wages and cost of nursing, as Pettenkofer was the first to do for Germany. The idea of guarding against material loss doubtless contributed substantially to the upswing of hygiene.

A serious deficiency still existed, however, in the social-economic health system, and it led to the very important researches in assimilation which Pettenkofer and his pupil and friend Carl von Voit carried on through long years. Pettenkofer realized that a definite knowledge of the individual body-household, its qualitative and quantitative food requirements and the usability of the nourishment given to it, was an imperative prerequisite for the general housekeeping of every larger community and for the economic organization of life.

Munich University, under the efficient promotion of King Maximilian II, was beginning to be a rendezvous for eminent nature scientists. Through Pettenkofer's influence, his honored teacher, Liebig, had been induced to come to Munich. The gifted Voit was working in the physiological institute. Important practical results of the "law of conservation of energy" were beginning to be worked out in the physiological laboratories. Through years of painstaking research Voit had been able to trace the change of nitrogenous albumen into an organism, and he could specify exactly what elements in meat, milk, eggs, etc., go to the building of the human body. His object was to ascertain exactly the various details of food assimilation in a living body. It seemed impossible, however, to find out the changes in matter free from albumen, such as fats and carbohydrates. This could be done only by measuring the gaseous matter, carbonic acid and water that are eliminated through the skin and lungs. Voit turned to Pettenkofer, who was thirteen years older and lived in the same house, for advice. It was just his kind of problem.

Pettenkofer devised a plan that is a wonderful proof of his irrepressible technical genius in chemistry. He built his famous respiration apparatus, which, in the

opinion of the startled bureaucrats who had to pay the
bill, was no apparatus but a whole factory. The respiration apparatus was a living room made of tinplate,
with window, door, bed, table, chair, in which men
could remain without the least injury while all the animal functions—after overcoming the greatest technical
difficulties—could be exactly measured: the consumption of food, air and water, and the excretion of gases,
urine, excrement and water. The astonishing performance of this gigantic instrument may be conceived of
when one remembers that some 400,000 to 600,000
liters of air had to be examined every day. But now it
was possible to ascertain exactly how much matter a
man used up in every one of his manifold activities
and requirements of life, awake or asleep, in physical
or mental work, with good or bad food.

The bold project was carried through with the help
of the king, who showed a keen interest in it and later
passed an hour in the respiration apparatus. He spent
7000 florins of his private funds on it.

The results justified the outlay. It was now possible
for the first time to get an accurate idea of everything
that was necessary, physically, to sustain the life of
man. No war can be carried on, no organization for
food requirements can be successful, no wage question
or problem of mass economy can be solved without
thorough consideration of the values then discovered in

albumen, fat and carbohydrates for the living requirements of the individual. Not only the normal food requirements of the body, but also those in illness, and
the impossibility of replacing albumen with any other
raw material, were discovered in principle by Voit and
Pettenkofer.

In 1854 cholera entered Pettenkofer's home. He
himself fell ill of the epidemic, but quickly recovered.
His cook died in the hospital and his second twin
daughter Anna came near to death. "These experiences naturally came very close to me and prompted
me to investigate the ways of cholera."

This simple sentence says much more about the
origin of acts of genius than libraries of pathographies
and psychological treatises of great pretensions. A
genius is often nothing but a normal and faithful
citizen in the sphere of the extraordinary. The much-
talked-of passions of genius, its much-discussed relations with insanity, on closer view are to be distinguished from everyday passions only by their trend
and their object. The life of every otherwise insignifi-
cant man is filled with passions and emotional im-
pulses which, if isolated from the poor, narrow frame
of an average life, would have to be regarded as morbid. The local columns of every newspaper give a disturbing glimpse of the daily pandemonium.

Every activity backed by understanding and directed

fearlessly and right-mindedly toward a great goal must lead to a great result. One can see a thing anew and for the first time only when one sees it under changed conditions. For this reason progress without genuine emotion is unthinkable. The courage to press on over the threshold of the ordinary into the realm of new tasks and the hitherto unseen goal also is decisive here. As one gets up to see who has knocked at the door, so a man like Pettenkofer, whose domestic peace the fist of cholera has disturbed, rises to investigate what cholera is. A question rightly stated is half solved.

This declaration of war on the fearful disease that like a threatening shadow of human helplessness darkened the proud progress of the nineteenth century, henceforth never again left his life free, carried it to its highest triumph, but also carried it to a tragic and touching conclusion.

Pettenkofer attacked the epidemic with his approved strategic methods. The freeing of the city and the land was the great object; the fate of single cases was to influence him as little as the fate of individual soldiers influences a general. For the science that deals with epidemics the individual is only the tiny cell of the great organism—the country, the continent, the earth—which the disease has struck down in the tumult. On the great map of the Bavarian general staff he marked all the places that had been attacked by cholera; red for those completely swept by the disease, green for those less seriously attacked, blue for towns with only scattered cases. For Munich a location book was made, in which almost two thousand fatal cases were registered by streets, houses, stories. The space between houses, the drinking water, the laundry, the locality, the living room, the temperature, the rain, the social surroundings—all the details of the environment of the sick became the object of his study.

At once men became aware of many essential peculiarities of the course of the epidemic which they had not noticed before. In 1855 appeared a preliminary report of the cholera commission, followed in 1857 by the complete report. They contained the hypotheses of his much-contested soil or nidus theory, to which he held to the end of his life.

Six weeks after the outbreak of the epidemic Pettenkofer announced his ideas for the first time at one of the frequent sessions of the Munich physicians. A little later (October 13) his theory had taken on its classic form:

"The origin of cholera is due essentially to (a) the germ or ferment, which in itself causes no cholera in the human organism, (b) a material or soil which receives the first factor and as a result thereof passes into a fermentation or budding, from which (c) a local miasma arises, which can cause cholera when it is not left to develop in that place and is breathed in by men at a certain degree of concentration. In other words, the sick man furnishes the soil for the harmless germ, the germ utilizes the soil as a ferment to develop the miasma, and this under certain conditions generates the cholera."

This hypothesis seems absurd to us today, but in order to understand it we must remember that in 1854 the cell pathology of Virchow (1857) was still unknown, bacteriology was still in its earliest infancy, and almost thirty years were still to be added to history before the true cholera germ, the comma bacillus, was discovered by Robert Koch (1883). Against the doctrine of miasma, of the production of disease by the fermenting process of decaying matter, there was the old doctrine of Contagium animatum, of the "illness excitant," which gave way at first very slowly; it was championed especially by the eminent German clinical doctor, Jacob Henle (1840), under the impression that he had discovered sickness-producing parasites and funguses. In 1849 the splenitis bacillus was discovered by Pollender. In 1873 Obermeier discovered in the germs of intermittent fever—the recurrent spirochaetae—the first originators of a human disease; and then the great era of Pasteur and Koch led bacteriological science to an intoxicating victory.

For Pettenkofer's time the alternative, contagion or miasma, was still a wholly unsolved problem of the highest explosive power. He himself was a convinced disciple of Liebig, who had written a convincing— though mistaken—chemical explanation of the miasma theory. Pettenkofer, who was far more a chemist than a physician, instinctively yielded to Liebig's reasoning; he thought in chemical terms, while bacteriology thought in pathological-anatomical terms. The ever-changing war of these two opposing forces, the Bavarian and the Prussian, as one might call them, took on a coloring of passion because of this fundamental difference in their methods of thought. But this breath of fanaticism was also due in part to the fact that the subject of the strife was so disturbing a public misfortune.

The splendor and prosperity of Europe rang like a powerful melody through the world. Every city, every state wished to drive the now-unfettered civilization a bit farther. World's fairs, those reviews of political pomp and endowment, were devised. London began them in 1851, the Paris of Napoleon III followed in 1855. In a few weeks Munich had erected its Glass Palace, and on July 15, 1854, in the presence of the kings of Prussia and Saxony had formally opened its General Exhibition of Industries and Industrial Products. A few days later the city, overrun with strangers, was depopulated by the terrible cry, "Cholera!" The continuous ringing of the death bells had to be forbidden. All who could get away fled from the city. Dancing and pleasure-seeking, the accompaniments of every deep anxiety, were the rage among those who remained, and the clergy raised a warning voice against them. The police forbade the death carts to gallop, but haste does what it has to do, and the churchyards were overfilled. Thus death reveled in Pettenkofer's beloved city.

Its raging, however, was not without limits. Pettenkofer saw very clearly that there were places and spots where the disease in general did not spread. These were almost always the higher sections built on rock. For a long time he could not decide whether these localities affected the germ itself or reduced the susceptibility of the people. According to his statistics the fluctuations of the disease in Munich followed slavishly the fluctuations of the underground water level. When the water sank deep, the danger of the epidemic climbed, and when the ground water rose the epidemic was extinguished. This time-place conditioning of the disease is the kernel of Pettenkofer's theory! The infection must come from the nidus which produced the dangerous change in the germs, and which went into the earth with human excretions. In no way was the drinking water responsible for the spread of the disease. He closes his statement: "I lay these views before my judges, not with an altogether steady but with a fearless hand, and hope that they will stir up war, a war for the good of all."

His hope was fulfilled.

Pettenkofer's theory was a characteristic linking of the contagious and miasmatic hypotheses. In important points it was wrong—and yet it performed an undying service in the development of the theory of disease. In the moment of peace before the impending storm-and-stress period of bacteriology, Pettenkofer, with his temperamental authority, had once more pitted the undeniable facts of epidemiology against the radicalism of a one-sided bacteriology which still recognized only a primitive schematic relation between excitant and disease.

His achievement consists in the gathering of facts, not in the incomplete or false conclusions drawn from them. Why did many centrally located places such as Lyons, Versailles, remain entirely free from cholera? Why were parts of Munich, Nuremberg, Traunstein, Würzburg not affected? Why were some houses or families inside of affected areas left entirely untouched, though their surroundings were the same? Why a sudden lessening of cholera in Munich and a sudden increase in the same year?

Pettenkofer studied these elementary problems with

wide-open eyes and keen mind, but he solved them only in very small part. He had as yet no conception of immunity, of disposition and constitution in our sense of the words. Bacteria and serums were still unknown. But even to the present day, with all our modern and exact means and methods, his problems still remain in large part unsolved riddles; and even after bacteriology has ceased to be the sole monarch, there are still countless researches in geo-medicine that link up immediately with Pettenkofer's theory. Even the latest bacteriological researches in regard to the variability of infections, the changes in virulence and the power of harmless bacteria to become poisonous, still leave a place for Pettenkofer's hypothesis of time-place factors in the origin of disease.

He has the great merit of having lent his support to the neurotic fear of bacteria. The fumigation and puncturing of postal parcels was adopted at his suggestion, and tormenting quarantines and separations were in large part discontinued. Doubtless he went too far in the rejection of measures of personal disinfection. In their place, however, he did some magnificent work in ground sanitation and in his passionate insistence on cleanliness. The Munich sewer system is his work, put through in spite of decades of opposition. Munich has him to thank for its good spring water, brought from mountain sources thirty-six kilometers away.

The construction of a central slaughterhouse was first achieved here. Out of a breeding-place of disease, out of a constant source of typhus Pettenkofer made one of the cleanest and healthiest cities in Europe. The people of Munich often called his physiological institute the "hypothesis palace." Pettenkofer's work proves that a creative practical understanding is not to be killed by the most daring hypotheses.

These undeniable and practical results of his labors gave his theories an injurious preeminence. His authority grew. In 1865 he became the first regular professor of hygiene, thereby winning academic recognition of his department. At the cholera conferences of 1867 and at the first conference called by the Reich in 1873, as well as at the international conference in Vienna a year later, he was the dominating figure. At Bismarck's suggestion he was chosen as president of the Imperial Health Commission in 1876, but he wisely declined to take this leap into the hostile Berlin atmosphere.

The opposition to his all-too-vigorous rejection of disinfection was constantly growing. Koch's discovery of the cholera bacillus gave a decisive blow to Pettenkofer's theory, and now Pettenkofer found in Virchow an ever stronger opponent wielding ever heavier weapons. The mass experiment of the Hamburg cholera epidemic in August, 1892, which sacrificed thousands within a few weeks in spite of a perfect sewer system, seemed to contradict the nidus theory completely. But Pettenkofer would not give up. He was seventy-six years old and had accumulated the experiences of a lifetime in his large, wise head; he had followed the trail of disease all over Europe, had studied thousands of cases in connection with epidemics, and these absolutely contradicted the communicability of the disease from man to man, yes, even the direct infectiousness of the germ itself. So he resolved, a few weeks after the threatening occurrence of the Hamburg epidemic, to undertake the famous, heroic experiment on himself.

He got Professor Gaffsky to send him a fresh culture of cholera bacilli from pest-ridden Hamburg. On October 7, 1892, he swallowed something like a thousand millions of the dangerous germs—many more than ever enter the body in a natural infection—after having first rendered the stomach acids ineffective by means of carbonate of soda.

There was probably no convinced bacteriologist at that time who would not have predicted his certain death. No material disturbance of his health occurred; only an enormous increase of bacteria in the intestine was noted. The miracle was wrought. The demonstration was complete: not every infection generates illness.

Pettenkofer wrote a sort of last will and testament regarding his experiment:

"Even if I had been deceiving myself and the experiment had been dangerous, I would have looked death in the face calmly, for it would have been no light-minded, cowardly suicide; I should have been dying in the service of science like a soldier on the field of honor. Health and life are, of course, as I have often said, precious earthly blessings; but they are not the highest that man can have. The man who wishes to stand higher than the animals must be ready to sacrifice even life and health for higher ideal possessions."

The great heroic act, nevertheless, was unable to accomplish its purpose. It is strange how slight is the power of a sacrifice to convince an unbelieving world. The experiment was repeated a dozen times by Pettenkofer's pupil, Emmerich, and other physicians. Nobody died. Some, however, were seriously ill. Pettenkofer was strengthened in his mistaken nidus theory, and his act did indeed create consternation among his opponents; but they simply would not believe what they saw, "because nothing can be that does not dare to be."

Not until much later was the proper interpretation of Pettenkofer's self-infection discovered; namely, that bacteria alone are by no means enough to explain the facts of an epidemic, and that the place-time conditions affirmed by Pettenkofer—on a mistaken hypothesis, of course—here play a part which has never yet been fully explained, important though we know it to be.

It was as if Pettenkofer's act of youthful daring had used up the old man's strength. He saw himself facing a new, hard, strange epoch. Nothing is more terrible than to strain all one's powers to make oneself understood, to give out one's last breath in something more than a cry, and to have it die away unheard. His band of pupils grew smaller. In 1890 his wife died. Two sons and a daughter lay buried. In 1894 he began to lay aside his responsibilities, one by one, like a man who is going to rest. First the work of teaching, then the office of court apothecary, then the presidency of the Academy, then his places on medical committees. He lingered in Seeshaupt on the Starnberger See and tended his trees or guided his heavily laden boat. Or he wandered through the streets of his home city, Munich, in a wide woolen cloak, his slouch hat jammed on his forehead, and gossiped with the last friend of his school days, an old chorus singer in the State Theater. At eighty-two he climbed daily the 122 steps to his tower dwelling in the court residence.

For the first time in his life Pettenkofer fell ill in January, 1901, at the age of eighty-three. A stubborn inflammation of the throat tortured him, doomed him to intolerable inactivity. He had passed into another century, and the world looked dismal. All that he had loved had left him. His memory would not hold for a day. His great, guarded treasure, his knowledge, was leaving him. The new ideas held by the people around him seemed to him strange and suspicious. He feared the poverty of the last days.

His revolver from Seeshaupt missed fire. Erect as ever, he went down the 122 steps, entered a gunshop, and made his last purchase. Someone followed him and begged him to do no harm to himself. With all his force of will he persisted in his purpose. The family watched his every step. He promised to travel and went to his room. It was the ninth of February, 1901. That night about eleven o'clock he shot himself.

THE OUTLOOK

Harvey Cushing, the Brain Surgeon, a Type of the Future Scientist

X

THE OUTLOOK

*Harvey Cushing, the Brain Surgeon, a Type of the
Future Scientist*

THE boundary of the twentieth century is passed.
At this point there is danger that our historical
sketch will develop into a critical examination of the
times. Therefore we pause. It would be a bad, bold
venture, at the end of a book which proves nothing
but the independent and guiding function of the Idea
in science, to take over the questionable rôle of contemporary critic.

A critic judges and takes sides. An eye-witness tells
what he sees. How often he, too, is mistaken, any law-
court proceedings will show. To be a trained and
earnest eye-witness—that is a worthwhile calling in
the service of nascent truth. We have seen how vital
it is to state a question rightly, but it is far more vital
to see an experience rightly. The retina is no focusing
lens. In the age of photography the art of seeing has
undergone an enormous change and expansion.

Has the "intercourse with ideas" become more humane in our time? Or are science and passion still inseparable? We will not decide that. No age knows the total of its martyrs. What truth among us is vainly seeking a hearing—this only later generations can recognize. Our century began with magnificent feats of research. Atom physics, the relativity and quantum theories, the discovery of the electromagnetic waves, the light theory, colloidal chemistry, synthetic textiles, the hormone doctrine, the discovery and creation of vitamins, aviation, the development of technical science by leaps and bounds, this magic world in whose midst we are living our lives, going through it almost reeling, inspired, shocked, stirred to the depths—if we do not belong to the sad company of dullards—are we equal to it all? As individuals in limited circles, perhaps we are; but by no means as a whole. Breathless, man goes striding along behind his ever more gigantic and more powerful creations, but often this adaptation expert can no longer leap across the chasm between his possibilities and his actualities. The results of this tragic conflict—wars, social catastrophes—threaten our future and destroy our poor and brief chance to share one step in the great procession of existence.

After the world concept of "classical physics," once believed to be forever constant, the results of the theoretical physics of the present day are preparing the way for a powerful revolution in our view of things in general, in our way of looking at nature, in our thought. Kant's fundamental ideas of space and time, the iron law of causality, these appear to be shattered. The ultimate effects of this new view of nature —upon technics, daily life, ethics, yes, even upon the sacred domain of religious faith—are beyond our range of vision. We who are still without the necessary perspective can only reverently surmise what is to come. The eternal question as to the final will of God is more burning than ever.

When we come to the scientific outlook of our day, we think of T. E. Lawrence, who began as an archeologist, became a soldier, adventurer, politician, flier, translator of Homer, finally devoted himself to the solving of technical scientific problems, wanted to be alone, and with his motorcycle dashed out his life against a tree. Or we think of Lindbergh, who as a youth flew over the ocean, and then studied the growth of cells in isolated organs in a year's work with the biologist, Carrel.

In order to avoid any hypothetical survey of human greatness and scientific genius, we will close with the description of a life-work that fixes the standard of inspired research—past, present and future—as the *organic unity of daring and knowledge.*

Harvey Cushing was thirty years old and had re-

ceived careful physiological and surgical training under Kocher in Bern, master of the operation for goiter,
when he returned in 1900 to Johns Hopkins University
in Baltimore. In Europe he had seen only one operation for a brain tumor, and that had to be given up as
impracticable by the eminent Kocher. The first operations for the removal of tumors from the brain had
been ventured upon in the '90's, but since then a series
of failures had plunged all leading surgeons into the
deepest pessimism. Brain tumors were regarded as
inoperable. Cures were miracles.

In 1901 a young girl in Johns Hopkins Hospital, in
the department of the famous Osler, died from some
obscure cause. The autopsy revealed an unsuspected
tumor at the base of the brain. Cushing was present.
"The discovery, during the dissection, of a wholly unsuspected and plainly inoperable tumor made a deep
impression on me."

Thirty years later, on August 15, 1931, Cushing was
writing the report of his two-thousandth brain operation. The woman operated upon had complained of
severe headaches and failing eyesight. With the aid of
a local anesthetic a patch of bone was raised and the
tissue cut electrically. With an aspirator the tumor was
removed from its bed; the bone flap was then replaced,
the wound exactly adjusted. After the operation was
over and the protecting cloths were removed, the

vision of both eyes was found to be restored, and the patient felt relief from her headache. Her progress was remarkable. In three days she was able to stand up, and in a week she could leave the hospital without danger. According to the last report, April 28, 1934, she was enjoying the best of health.

"In 1901," writes Cushing, "such a daring operation would have been regarded as wonderful. Thirty years from now, doubtless, our present operations will seem to our successors as crude as those of thirty years ago now seem to us." He recalls the saying of Leonardo da Vinci that "only a mediocre pupil does not surpass his teacher."

Cushing is the man who, by a lifelong, tenacious, systematic labor of genius, wrested from the grip of death those who had been hopelessly given up to die of brain tumors. For thirty years he has done nothing but operate for tumors on the brain. He has devoted his life, the lives of his assistants and nurses, the arrangements of his hospital, the hours of every day, the mechanics of every movement to the service of this one single thing—operating on brain tumors. Neurological diagnoses were steadily improved, the means for X-raying the cerebral ventricles by injection of air was contrived (by Dandy), and in 1927 came the electric knife, creating entirely new conditions in operating and greatly reducing the danger of bleeding.

Most important of all, however, was the absolutely unique technical organization with whose aid Cushing's scalpel did its work.

"The patients usually lie several hours on the operating table after an operation, until consciousness is fully restored, and then they often tarry several days in the operating room. Patients with trouble in swallowing must often be fed a long time through the nose." While the doctors are operating, a special corps of helpers devote their undivided attention to the thirty or forty patients who are usually under treatment at the same time, ready to act if the slightest untoward symptom appears. Cushing has brought it about that the fatalities from the four worst kinds of brain tumors, which in his practise in 1901–1912 still amounted to 30.9, 13.5, 21, and 25 per cent, in the years 1928–1931 were reduced to 11, 5.7, 7.7, and 4.4 per cent. That is an annihilating victory over death.

A. W. Meyer, himself a prominent surgeon, several years ago gave us this brilliant description of one of Cushing's operations:

"The greatest impression on every visitor to clinics in the United States is undoubtedly that made by Cushing. Words cannot convey what one experiences there! Cushing operates only a few times in the week, and then does only a single operation in a day. . . . All the preparations for the operation have begun an

hour or two before he appears. The patient is brought
in. He is suffering from a tumor in the brain, and as a
result of it his right hand is paralyzed.

"Cushing appears in his light gray operating garb,
high at the neck, and wearing the cap that goes with
it. He steps at once to the side of the patient and
speaks a few friendly words to him. The man is laid
on the operating table, his head is washed with alcohol, and immediately Cushing begins very thoughtfully and slowly with the local anesthesia. During the
operation the patient appears occasionally to fall
asleep. With his scalpel Cushing now makes a scratch
indicating the cut, then binds a thick gauze bandage
over his own mouth and nose, ties it carefully over his
head above the cap, and secures the knot still further
with a safety pin. I mention this as a small and naturally unessential illustration, but it characterizes so
fully the complete carefulness, certainty, reliability and
thoughtfulness that distinguish him and his operations
and produce the results that have become world-
famous!

"While Cushing now washes his hands the patient
is placed in position and prepared. A frame leaves his
face entirely free for his own view of the doctor; free
also to the observation of the skilful sister who sits in
a low, comfortable chair beside the operating table, the
blood-pressure apparatus in her hand, and constantly

makes notes. The diathermy electrodes are carefully wrapped, and a continuous dropping of saline solution warmed between two hot-water bags begins with the operation. The cutting of the bone and the final washing are cared for by Cushing himself. Specially prepared cloths with a hole in them and provided with strings are fastened by him almost hermetically around the field of operation, so that a slip is impossible. The inner edge on the operating side is sealed with gutta-percha tissue. Everything is done with the greatest care and thoroughness according to a definite system.

"Three physicians are assisting, and a trained man and woman help with the instruments. Their team work is incomparable. One notes their joy in knowing, even beforehand, what the operator will need. When the skull is opened, the assistants automatically attach the reflector lamp on the surgeon's forehead. The electrical cautery knife is handled by a special technician. The method of erecting the operating table above the patient, the aspirator for keeping the opening drained, the diathermy, everything is part of a wonderfully organized system.

"One must have seen the work of Cushing's expressive hands to appreciate it: what should go slowly goes slowly, what should go fast goes with lightning speed. Scarcely a drop of blood flows. . . . At the close of the operation Cushing lays the brain lobes back as he wishes them to be, and there is no longer a hollow. The warm saline all this time has steadily kept the brain from becoming chilled. Every surface of the brain that does not have to be seen during the operation is covered with bits of wadding, constantly renewed, and everything is done with the greatest gentleness. At the end not a speck of blood is to be seen. If one had not seen it with his own eyes he would declare it a miracle! The patient, now fully conscious, speaks cheerfully, and the hand that was paralyzed a few minutes ago grips firmly the proffered hand of his physician! That wonderful operation was a joy to me such as I never before experienced."

Thus has a scientist of our century, a man who lives among us, dared to lay hands on the tenderest and most secret substance of our bodies, the brain, the motor of human power and greatness.

The electric current, anesthetics, definite knowledge of the anatomical structure of tissue, the circulation of the fluids of the body, the physiological functions, hygienic technique, all these sacred blessings of research, toilsomely acquired through the centuries, brought together amid torture and danger, guarded and added to amid solitude and distress of conscience, scorn and hatred, are united in the hand of one man, who, many times every week in his operating room, amid breathless silence, would free the human body of evil growths and suffering. This hand, which is inspired by the heart and made skilful by the head, which bears responsibility, which is cautious and bold, this science-hand is the symbol of the Idea that calls life back from death, and for which to live and to die is the highest human distinction.

WHEN PAVLOV VISITED AMERICA

When "Trail-Blazers of Science" was published last autumn in Berlin—under its original title, "Das Leben für die Idee"—the author sent a copy of it to Dr. Harvey Cushing, the only living subject treated in its pages. Dr. Cushing responded with the following letter to Dr. Gumpert, which is so interesting that it is reproduced here—with the kind permission of both doctors:

YALE UNIVERSITY

THE SCHOOL OF MEDICINE

NEW HAVEN   CONNECTICUT

November 19, 1935.

DEAR DR. GUMPERT:

I received with pleasure a few days ago the copy of your *Das Leben für die Idee* and took it home to read without the slightest warning—until I had almost finished the book—that I had been included among the persons with whom you were dealing.

I feel honored and at the same time embarrassed, for I am of course aware that I do not properly belong with those whose biographies comprise the bulk of your volume. I can only account for my name having been included by the fact that my dear old and greatly admired friend, Hans Horst Meyer of Vienna, turned up at the Physiological Congress in Boston six years ago accompanied by his son Arthur.

Pavlov, who of course was the central figure in the Congress, was very anxious to see an operation for brain tumor, so it was arranged one day that a group of his friends, mostly the Russian delegation, should quietly come to the Brigham Hospital for the purpose.

299

On the appointed day, I took them first to see the patient, who happened to be a left-handed young man with a temporal lobe tumor on the right side. In this Pavlov was greatly interested because he too had familial left-handedness.

The operation went off very well; the tumor, which was partly cystic, was easily exposed, and by electrosurgical methods the mural nodule was easily excised. At this juncture, Pavlov became so excited that he almost fell off the box on which he was standing looking over my shoulder.

After the operation I secured a piece of liver from the hospital kitchen so that Pavlov might try out the electrical currents to see what their cutting and coagulating properties were. He finally ended up by writing his name on the lobe of liver with the electrical needle, and it is now in the Museum of the Harvard Medical School, or should be, for I at least thought it was interesting enough to be sent over there for preservation.

Arthur Meyer was so entertained by this whole episode that when he returned home he wrote a little account of it, I believe, in the *Wiener klinische Wochenschrift*, of which he sent me a copy.

It is this article, I suppose, that you have seen and drawn upon for your sketch, and while very much complimented, I thought you might be interested to know something about the circumstances which led to its having been written.

You may possibly have known A. W. Meyer himself, and I hope also his father, who, I always felt, occupied a position with you in Austria such as William H. Welch held with us, as the accredited doyen of the profession.

The rest of the book has of course interested me greatly, for I collect the published writings of most of the people with whom you have dealt, and indeed have almost a complete Vesalian collection of several hundred volumes. Your essays consequently have given me pleasure, for they not only show historical research but have been written with unusual charm.

Sincerely yours,
[signed] HARVEY CUSHING

INDEX